DATA/INFORMATION AVAILABILITY

Edited by
RALPH I. COLE

The American University
Technology of Management Series
PAUL W. HOWERTON, *General Editor*

THOMPSON BOOK COMPANY
WASHINGTON, D.C.

Library of Congress Catalog Card No. 66-25651

Printed in the United States of America

FOREWORD

In a recent Institute held under the auspices of the Center for Technology and Administration of the American University, the subject of the "Availability of Data/Information" was treated in appreciable depth. Those papers which tended to highlight the issues of information availability have been edited and related to one another in a forceful way by Ralph I. Cole, Director of Institutes and Special Programs in the Center.

The meeting has stimulated "thinking in depth" in the subject area as is demonstrated by the returns we had from the participants. By participants we mean both the distinguished group of speakers and the highly articulate attendees. The speakers brought a wide variety of well-informed backgrounds and interest to the consideration of the subject. We owe them a debt of gratitude for their meaningful contributions to the information sciences.

We do not represent this collection of opinions as an agreed position on how to manage the availability of Data/Information, because we feel that there is no one demonstrably superior method. We try to present the issues both existing and potential with some indication of tested solutions to identified problems.

Paul. W. Howerton
General Editor

PREFACE

The papers selected for presentation herein represent but a few of the more important aspects of data generation, format, storage retrieval and utilization which concern the management of technology.

The first two papers in Part I treat the history and growth of data handling, particularly those aspects which concern *structuring* explicit meanings to chemical and biological data Elements when used in conjunction with electronic methods for Filing and Retrieval. The third paper of Part I attempts to look into the future of "computerized" information handling and commands considerable attention.

Part II consists of two papers dealing with the science of management and the relationships that exist to both technological advances and decision-making, all referenced against the oncoming rush of knowledge.

Part III deals with Data/Information sources and their Utility and represents the experience of five distinguished speakers each selecting but one aspect to explore.

Part IV includes three papers each treating a different and difficult aspect of improving the structure, content, and usefulness of data.

Without question the field of Data/Information suffers from a lack of formal structure and guidance that will be benefited from a study of these discussions. Judging from the laments of managers, greatly increased effort in this particular area is sorely needed.

Ralph I. Cole
Editor

LIST OF CONTRIBUTORS

ALBERT N. ABAJIAN

Consultant specializing in diversified Management and Economic Research. Lecturer and Author. Among his credits are "A Proposed Coordinated System for International Commercial-Economic Communication in the Government," prepared for a subcommittee of the U.S. Senate, and "EPIC–Economic Progress Through International Communication." He is a fellowship graduate of the International Marketing Institute of the Harvard Graduate School of Business Administration, and Research Associate, the Center for Technology and Administration, The American University.

ROBERT L. BIRCH

Reference Librarian affiliated with the U. S. Patent Office. Specialist in data recovery and related techniques and fields. Frequent contributor to information science literature as a lecturer, teacher, and author.

RALPH I. COLE

Director, Institutes and Special Programs, The Center for Technology and Administration, and Professorial Lecturer, the American University, Washington, D.C. Well-known technology and management consultant in research and development administration in both industry and government. Frequent lecturer, author and contributor in the management-information effectiveness area. Awarded Legion of Merit for his contribution to Air Force and Signal Corps research administration. Engineering Manpower Commissioner. Fellow of the IEEE and a member of numerous professional and technical societies.

CHARLES DE VORE

Deputy Executive Assistant for Scientific Information, Office of Naval Research, Washington, D.C. Well-known author and executive in broad areas of scientific and technical information, both in government and in industry. Frequent lecturer, writer, and participant in national managerial-scientific meetings. Member, IEEE and AAAS.

C. STARK DRAPER

Director of Instrumentation Laboratory, and Professor, Massachusetts Institute of Technology. Distinguished inventor in fields of aeronautics, in control, and in space, in which he has made outstanding contributions.

He has often been honored for these achievements both here and abroad. Well-known lecturer and author in broad areas of scientific research and in research management. Substantial contributor to the scientific literature of our day. Honored member of many technical and professional societies. Listed in *Who's Who in America.*

PAUL W. HOWERTON

Director of the Center for Technology and Administration and Visiting Professor, The American University, Washington, D.C. Teacher, lecturer, writer and consultant in the technology of management and more particularly in cybernetics, electronic data processing, information sciences, chemistry, mathematics, and linguistics. Former Deputy Assistant Director for Central Reference of the CIA where he was awarded the Intelligence Medal for Merit for his work in developing information control systems and in computational linguistics. Member of many professional societies both here and abroad. Fellow of the AAAS. Member of Sigma Xi.

AUGUSTUS C. JOHNSON

Noted mathematician-consultant affiliated with Booz-Allen Applied Research, Inc., Frequent contributor in such areas as operations research-linear programming involving industrial and government distribution problems as well as the entire field of logistics. Also in the design and operation of data-collection systems for space-environment tests, as well as a wide variety of systems analysis programs. Lecturer and author. Member of the Society for Industrial and Applied Mathematics.

F. ELLIS KELSEY

Assistant to the Surgeon General, U.S. Public Health Services. Well-known authority, writer, teacher, and consultant in information sciences, particularly difficult aspects of information abstracting, indexing, storage, and retrieval of advanced chemical-biological literature interfaces.

HAROLD F. LANIER

Manager, Advanced Technology Division, Goodyear Aerospace Corporation. Noted technology and management-sciences executive with outstanding credits in guided-missile programs and in research-development administration, both in the government and in industry. Well-known lecturer and contributor with a deep involvement in the managerial implications of advancing technology, as well as in the information sciences.

G. S. SIMPSON

Battelle Memorial Institute Executive, concerned with major responsibility for administration of specialized information centers. Noted lecturer, authority in the information sciences field, more particularly in the management of information centers. Frequent participant in the coordination of interdisciplinary research in such areas as aeronautical, aerospace, electronics, defense, and the biosciences–to name but a few.

JOHN I. THOMPSON

President, John I. Thompson and Company, Washington, D.C. Noted technology and managerial executive specializing in research and development management, including a deep involvement in the information sciences area. Well-known lecturer, and author, recognized as an outstanding authority in many facets of research and development administration.

MORRIS M. THOMPSON

Deputy Assistant Chief Topographic Engineer for Research and Technical Standards, U. S. Geological Survey. Noted aerial topographer, frequent lecturer, writer, and contributor in various aspects of photogrammetry. Fellow, AAAS and ASCE. Editor-in-chief, *Manual of Photogrammetry,* published by the American Society of Photogrammetry (1965).

ISAAC D. WELT

Deputy Director of the Center for Technology and Administration, and Research Professor, The American University, Washington, D.C. Noted teacher, lecturer, writer, and consultant in chemistry and information sciences, more particularly in abstracting, indexing and retrieval aspects. Active in the cardiovascular literature project of the National Academy of Sciences since its inception, and its Director, 1955-1961. Associate Director of the Institute for Advancement of Medical Communication prior to its Cardiovascular Literature Program becoming affiliated with the Center for Technology and Administration in 1964. Author of many scientific papers and frequent contributor and editor of information science volumes. Member of numerous scientific and professional societies.

THOMAS WINTERFIELD

Senior Analyst, National Oceanographic Data Center. Experienced geologist and oceanographer specializing in such matters as physical properties of sea water, etc. Prominent in information sciences, more particularly in the data format, data processing, and retrieval aspects.

CONTENTS

Page

Preface iii
Foreword v
List of Contributors vii

Part I. CURRENT DEVELOPMENTS IN DATA SOURCE, TECHNIQUE, AND FUTURE TRENDS

1. Biological Data/Information Centers and the Future 3

ISAAC D. WELT
Center for Technology and Administration

Libraries have traditionally assumed responsibility for most of the important functions of Information Centers in many areas of science, particularly in biomedicine. Plans for such centers are therefore mainly concerned with the handling of documents. Acquisition, processing, abstracting, indexing, and dissemination of documents are certainly proper functions of Information Centers, although the needs of research personnel cannot be fully met by this type of operation. Methods must therefore be evolved for the detailed analysis and evaluation of document *content* in whatever depth is necessary.

2. Storage and Retrieval of Chemical and Biological Data ... 17

F. ELLIS KELSEY
Public Health Service, Department of Health, Education and Welfare

Efforts to relate chemical structure to biological activity, originating in the work of Erlich, have depended on accurate knowledge of chemical structure and reactivity. Although the characteristics of most biological processes are as yet ill-defined, many relationships to well-understood chemical compounds have been established. Future developments depend on the capacity to organize both chemical and biological knowledge in a form that will permit the use of electronic methods for filing and finding. A long step in this direction is the plan to provide a completely computerized file of all known chemical structures, and to use this resource for substructural generic searches. The next step, an analogous file for biological information, is the challenge of today.

3. Data-Retrieval Growth Possibilities 31

CHARLES DE VORE
Office of Naval Research
Washington, D.C.

Acquiring essential engineering data promptly and organizing it for most effective retrieval is understandably of great concern to the Department of Defense, from the standpoint of developing possible solutions to engineering problems as well as with the operational use of such solutions. An outstanding example of a long-range program, involving a multiuse computer network, is Project MAC—for Multiple-Access Computer and Machine Aided Cognition.

Part II. THE SCIENCE OF MANAGEMENT AND DATA/INFORMATION

4. Relationship Between Availability of Data and Significant Technological Advances 43

C. STARK DRAPER
Massachusetts Institute of Technology

Advances in technology so new that pertinent data are few must depend upon human creativity and motivations. Progress in well developed technology requires complete and wisely chosen data documented for storage and retrieval. These principles are illustrated with samples drawn from operations of the Instrument Laboratory at M.I.T.

5. The Role of Technical Information in Decision-Making ... 55

HAROLD F. LANIER
Goodyear Aerospace Corporation

Much of our information-handling structure is predicated on the assumption that technical information is either (1) secretly held for exploitation by the owner, or (2) fully authenticated and published for the general use of the technical community with, however, recourse to patent safeguards, or (3) that which is selectively distributed as part of the combined industry/government research and development program planning. In this latter area, technical information is usually neither complete nor authenticated, rather a "sample" that is but a prediction of the real "flow" to come. Such is the data that is exchanged between customers and vendors as they make their response to the government's request for new research and development projects. The acquisition, verification, and utilization of semiavailable technical information is discussed, particularly as it concerns those phases of R & D from program inception through preliminary systems engineering.

Part III. SPECIALIZED DATA/INFORMATION SOURCES AND THEIR UTILITY

6. Functions of Data/Information Analysis Centers 71

G. S. SIMPSON, JR.
Battelle Memorial Institute

Based on letters and oral communications received from over thirty specialists, plus literature research, the functions of data/information analysis centers are discussed. While in selected details, the functions of analysis centers vary, in total their functions are similar. Analysis centers provide a scientific and technical intellectual analytical service to a specialized audience.

7. Patents: A Valuable Information Source for Research 87

PAUL W. HOWERTON
Center for Technology and Administration
The American University, Washington, D. C.

Patents constitute the most compact and easily identifiable technical literature resource available in which cause and effect are shown with minimum verbiage. One-sixth of all U. S. patents of a chemical or chemically related nature granted in 1963 were assigned to foreign companies and countries. Technical information on methods of manufacture, results of experimentation and utility of inventions is frequently revealed only in the pertinent patents and does not get into the usual journal literature. This point is particularly important in connection with patents granted in foreign countries to organizations within these countries. Examples of the richness of patents as a technical information source illustrate their potentialities.

8. NODC: An Experiment in Response to a Need for Scientific Integration 103

THOMAS WINTERFIELD
National Oceanographic Data Center
Washington, D. C.

The National Oceanographic Data Center (NODC) is designed to act as an integrating force in oceanography both nationally and internationally. First, it is an interagency activity integrating certain oceanographic activities of a number of government agencies and private industry. Through exchange agreements with more than thirty countries it furnishes a link between the national and international oceanographic efforts. Second, by acquiring, processing, archiving, and indexing nearly the entire spectrum of oceanographic data, it serves to integrate the various scientific disciplines which constitute oceanography. Third, through quality control, promotion of standardized formats and techniques, and formating of the basic archives, it serves to integrate the data-producing with the data-consuming activities.

9. Availability and Creative Uses of Topographic Data 113

MORRIS M. THOMPSON
Geological Survey, Washington, D.C.

Topographic information, consisting of quantitative and qualitative data on the nature of the earth's surface, is used creatively in the planning of major enterprises. Such information is usually presented in continuous form on maps. Potentially, automatic data-processing techniques can be used for the retrieval of topographic data.

10. EPIC: Economic Progress Through International Communications 133

ALBERT N. ABAJIAN
Research Associate, Center for Technology and Administration
The American University, Washington, D.C.

Expansion of exports is believed vital to the achievement of United States goals. Failure to increase exports sufficiently is a matter of urgent national policy. While world trade volume has increased more than 300 percent since 1946, the United States share has declined substantially. Potential American exporters lack pertinent information on foreign markets and will not risk capital on questionable ventures. A scientifically worldwide information-processing system is described which is believed essential for international business.

Part IV. IMPROVING THE STRUCTURING, CONTENT, AND USEFULNESS OF DATA

11. Use of Mathematical and Analytical Techniques on Organizing Data 151

AUGUSTUS C. JOHNSON
Booz-Allen Applied Research, Inc.
Bethesda, Md.

A discussion of the role of the experimental design in the handling of quantitative data, using a large space environment test facility as an example. A discussion is given on a nonrigorous intuitive basis of the application of some analytical tools.

12. Packaging, Labeling, and Finding Evaluated Technical Data.163

ROBERT L. BIRCH
Scientific Library, U. S. Patent Office

Large bodies of valuable evaluated technical data may become sandbars in the information mainstream unless they are packaged and labeled for retrievability. Labeling includes indication of the particular standard to which the units used belong. Representative publications relating to numerical data retrieval are listed.

13. Needs of Industry for Critical and Other Data Derived from Government Contracts 177

JOHN I. THOMPSON
John I. Thompson and Company, Washington, D.C.

Discusses the Government's handling of technical data and information of the type received under contracts; what such data is actually comprised of, their availability, and just what use industry should expect in its application of such data. Discrete illustrations serve to highlight the issues.

PART I

CURRENT DEVELOPMENTS IN DATA SOURCE, TECHNIQUE, AND FUTURE TRENDS

BIOLOGICAL DATA/INFORMATION CENTERS AND THE FUTURE

ISAAC D. WELT, PH.D.
Deputy Director for Scientific and Technical Information
Center for Technology and Administration
The American University

A rigorous definition of the terms "data" and "information" is needed before we venture to talk about them. Very few words have been as badly misused as this popular word *information*. Information science, information theory, information storage and retrieval are used synonymously with a total lack of regard for precision of language. The most flagrant abuse of the term is probably in describing a document storage and retrieval system. Here, there is a confusion between ends and means.

Ideally, the aim of an information center is to provide information. In practice, however, the vast majority of these organizations provide nothing more than unevaluated documents which, presumably, contain information. It is up to the user to extract pertinent information from this pile of printed material.

Document storage and retrieval systems have been discussed quite amply in the published literature of documentation as well as at numerous meetings, symposia, conferences, and workshops. In recent years mechanized methods for the handling of documents have come to the fore, involving either magnetic tape or photographic film as the storage medium for indexes to documents. Photographic film possesses the added economic advantage of being available, in microform, as a storage medium for documents as well.

The relationship between true data and information storage and retrieval, which is the subject of the present Institute, and what is generally described in the literature under that name, is close enough to have provided opportunity for confusion. There is a spectrum of activities, of a continuous nature, which embraces a good part, if not all, of the processes involved in scientific communication. It begins with data and ends with data.

First, we have the experimental data developed by the scientist and engineer in his laboratory, much of them in tabular or graphic form. Convention dictates that the results of research be written up for presentation at meetings or for publication in scientific journals. As a result, a superstructure of language is built around the data. Thus we have the historical introduction to the work, a description of apparatus and techniques, the actual data, a discussion of what the author thinks they mean, some polemics, a summary and a list of citations or references. This constitutes the conventional scientific paper.

Some time after its publication most scientists and engineers decry the time lag. The paper is abstracted by, we hope, a competent subject-matter authority. If the abstract is at all informative, it must contain something about methodology and conclusions. It does not usually contain the actual data. Still later on, the abstract, or perhaps the original paper itself, is indexed for accurate and efficient retrieval. Retrieval of what? Of the paper. In other words, this is indexing for document retrieval. An efficient document-retrieval system will greatly facilitate the writing of review articles, both critical and uncritical. To do so, the reviewer should read all of the pertinent documents, thereby becoming familiar with the data contained in them. He is actually synthesizing facts which are scattered among many journals in the literature. At this point in the spectrum, data collections become feasible and true information storage and retrieval appears. Laboratory data bearing on a particular problem can now be collected, published in the form of a handbook, or stored on magnetic tape or photographic film. Critical evaluation of the data by competent scientists and engineers is possible. We have arrived at the far end of the communication spectrum and once again are dealing with data rather than with documents. We can thus provide a service which is badly needed by almost all scientists and engineers–namely, specific answers to specific questions, such as the melting point of a chemical substance or the coefficient of expansion of a new alloy.

DATA/INFORMATION

The definition for data–or rather for datum–as given in Webster's *Second International Dictionary,* is perhaps adequate for our needs. Datum is defined as "a fact or principle granted or presented." In the field of science, it is most frequently of a quantitative nature, although not necessarily so. In the more advanced sciences, such as physics and astronomy, numerical values are most frequently encountered. In biology, on the other hand, data are more of a qualitative nature, such as, for example, "Epinephrine increases blood pressure upon its intravenous administration in the laboratory rat." It is perhaps more customary to consider the foregoing item as a piece of "information." There is no hard and fast distinction between the two terms as used by scientists.

NEEDS FOR DATA/INFORMATION CENTERS

It will be readily admitted that the data/information center has been sorely neglected as an integral part of the communication process in Science and Technology. The reasons for this unsatisfactory state of affairs are partly historical. The emphasis upon services providing only documents is an outgrowth of the practices of conventional librarianship. Librarians are well trained to provide answers to such questions as, for example, "Have you got a book about transistors?" At one time, reference librarians were able to answer specific questions, provided there was an encyclopedia or handbook available which contained the answers. This "look-up and see" type of service became obsolete many years ago because of the lack of suitable sources and because of the increasing technical complexity of the questions which scientists and engineers wanted answered. The nonscientific background of most reference librarians made communication between them and their questioners exceedingly difficult, for in order to answer a question one must first understand it.

Is there really a crying need for centers and services providing data to scientists and engineers? The potential users of such facilities have indeed indicated such a need. In a recent paper by Gove and Way,[1] physicists on the staff of the Nuclear Data Project, the following passage may be found.

> While many information specialists are concerned only with supplying a complete list of references, current or retrospective, this should be regarded as an intermediate goal. To be successful, information systems should provide the right information to the right person at the right time, in the right units, in the right language, with discrepancies or new trends clearly visible, and with a minimum amount of chaff. To design systems that will do this we need, among other things, better data compilations.
>
> Data compilations are most useful in active fields of science, fields in which new results are coming in rapidly and in which there

is some degree of confusion concerning how best to display and interpret these results. In these fields compilations can and should play an important role in the information cycle—that is, the process in which information is published, received, stored, retrieved, studied and finally used in the production of new information. As more and more documents pour in it becomes increasingly unpleasant to think of reading all the papers in one's own specialty plus all of those in related specialties and still have time for research. Even if present retrieval methods are developed to the limit of their capabilities and retrieve all, and only, the relevant articles there is still the job of reading them. In this regard the compilations can be used to ease the job of the researcher, at least in the borderline specialties. Compilations, if properly made and properly used, can save many hours of library searching.

Dr. Y. S. Touloukian, Director of the Thermophysical Properties Research Center at Purdue University testified before the Ad Hoc Subcommittee on a National Research Data Processing and Information Retrieval Center as follows[2]:

One sure thing we find, engineers do not want bibliographies, when we answer so authoritatively by providing bibliographic citations where all this information is, and the next inquiry is, "We have no physical possibility of getting access and getting in physical contact with this information, let alone our intellectual contact with it. Please tell us the result of your entering these sources of information, culling them, judging them, evaluating them, come forth with one statement as to the most probable answer that you feel as of today that you can establish as a result of evaluating this information".

Dr. Touloukian had many more cogent comments to make which I will quote later on.

In the course of these same hearings, Dr. Kelsey,[3] who is also our next speaker, stated "Systems should also be planned to isolate the individual fact from unneeded materials in the document or book in which that fact is located, in order to shorten the time required for the user to get to the facts he wants and to decrease the mass of information which must be transmitted to him so that he can get the single fact he wants". Later on, he added that "Ultimately, we should strive to retrieve information itself, rather than just the documents which contain the information".[4] This is precisely what the present Institute is all about!

In conclusion, reference must be made, as it has been by so many others before, to the excellent report entitled "Science, Government and Information," the Weinberg report.[5] On page 21, the distinction between document and information storage and retrieval is alluded to when administrators of information centers are cautioned: "The new system (i.e., most mechanized information systems) generally retrieve documents rather than information". It is on page 32, however, that the problem is most clearly stated.

> The centralized document depository is primarily a clearinghouse for documents; in general, it does not try to glean information from the documents it handles, but merely provides appropriate documents to users. But retrieval of documents is not the same as retrieval of information; a technical specialist really needs the information contained in the published literature, not the published literature itself. To retrieve information, as contrasted to documents, the technical community has devised the specialized data and information center.

PROBLEMS OF STAFFING

The next paragraph of the report states that "There are now in the United States some 400 such centers". This may be an overoptimistic figure, if an information center is defined as an organization which provides specific data and answers to specific questions rather than critical reviews and specialized bibliographies. There is no doubt that there is a severe shortage of such agencies, no matter how they are defined. Most of the emphasis has been placed in the past, and is still being focussed upon document retrieval services. The major reason for this state of affairs concerns the shortage of qualified personnel available and willing to carry on such professional activities. The staffing of data/information centers involves competent scientists, in addition to technical librarians, professional abstractors and indexers, translators and computer engineers. Only subject-matter specialists can answer the complicated questions of active scientists and engineers. As the Weinberg report (p.33) emphasizes:

> Such knowledgeable scientific middlemen *who themselves contribute to science* [*italics in original*] are the backbone of the information center; they make an information center a technical institute rather than a technical library. The essence of a good technical information center is that it be operated by highly competent working scientists and engineers—people who see in the operation of the center an opportunity to advance and deepen their own per-

> sonal contact with their science and technology. Proliferation of the specialized information centers will therefore require many such information scientists," dedicated and knowledgeable technical men, who help interpret and assimilate the literature for others working in the field.

We may come back to Dr. Touloukian again for another highly pertinent quotation[2] (p.183):

> In my judgment, the second phase which we consider to be the essence of the information problem, evaluated knowledge, takes specialists, highly trained in their fields; in our area, they could be physical chemists, physical metallurgists, chemical engineers, mechanical engineers, or physicists. These people, as they are found at academic institutions, or research and development laboratories of both government and industry, are prima donnas, and rightly so.

His solution to the personnel problem is that (p. 184):

> A researcher does not want to do data processing from 8 a.m. to 5 p.m. One wants to do his own individual research while he may be very much interested in contributing to this [i.e., scientific information activities] on a part-time basis. This is the way we can attract competent people at our own center, and from my observations this is the way people are attracted to other centers where such activities do take place.
>
> Specialists do want to keep their fingers in original research at least part time.
>
> This type of work has to be done in an environment which is indicated by the individuals themselves, by their pleasures of work, rather than as a job to be done upon the asking of someone else.

These comments represent wise counsel to both the fledgling and to the experienced manager or administrator of a science information system. Subject-matter specialists at the master's or doctorate level cannot, at least for the present, be eliminated by the introduction of computers, their associated "software" and their retinue of programmers, data processors, system engineers: the nursemaids of automation's progeny.

DOCUMENT RETRIEVAL IN ENGINEERING AND THE PHYSICAL SCIENCES

As has been pointed out, and particularly by Kelsey,[4] the success of data/information retrieval depends upon adequate and accurate document retrieval. One group is somewhat parasitic upon the other and no component of the system is stronger than its weakest link.

It is therefore encouraging to report that approximately 18 months ago, the Engineers Joint Council, representing (at that time) some eleven constituent societies and eighteen national associate, regional associate, and affiliate societies, decided to do something about the document retrieval problem in the engineering literature. As Costello and Wall[6] describe it, "an arrangement was completed with Battelle Memorial Institute whereby Battelle would offer publicly on a nationwide basis a course of instruction in abstracting and coordinate indexing". In other words, the engineers themselves are going to be responsible for the control of the products of their own intellectual metabolism and this is as it should be. It is also in line with Touloukian's comments, as quoted above, concerning the importance of subject-matter specialists in the information cycle and attempts to implement one of the section headings of the Weinberg report[5] (p. 26), "Authors must accept more Responsibility for Information Retrieval". The success of this venture, which is to be hoped for, will provide a "gold mine" of pertinent documents for the engineer-data/information scientist from which, after suitable refining operations, data will emerge for subsequent evaluation and widespread dissemination. We will know more about this, when according to Costello and Wall, "Battelle plans to hold a users' conference later in 18 months for all individuals who have completed the course at any of the sessions and other with dirty hands in the actual planning, designing, installation, and operation of concept-coordination systems in user situations. This conference will be for the purpose of exchange of ideas, techniques, and solutions to input and output problems, and generally for discussion of work done in individual situations which might be of benefit to personnel in other operating situations". An ambitious undertaking indeed, but a sine qua non for the subsequent development of comprehensive data and information in the exceedingly diversified areas of subject matter which constitute modern engineering practice.

The publication of the "Thesaurus of Engineering Terminology" has just been announced by the Engineers Joint Council. The result of nearly two years of work, it contains over 10,000 selected terms.

Another recent event designed to facilitate document retrieval in the physical and engineering sciences is the announcement by the Federal Council for Science and Technology that the Department of Commerce, through it Office of Technical Services, will provide a clearinghouse for all unclassified technical reports and translations generated by all government agencies. This will be done in cooperation with the Science Information Exchange and the National Referral Center for Science and Technology at the Library of Congress.[7]

The situation in chemistry, insofar as document retrieval is concerned, is relatively good. This is due primarily to the whole-hearted support of the American Chemical Society.

The American Institute of Physics has been carrying on a research program in documentation for several years.[8] One of the practical results has been a citation index to a number of Russian Physics journals.[9]

The American Meteorological Society published its Meteorological and Geoastrophysical abstracts, and is experimenting with computer-produced permuted title indexes which may lead to the successful mechanization of the Universal Decimal Classification scheme.[10]

The American Society of Mechanical Engineers has developed yet another computer-produced index, called WADEX.[11]

All of these activities, it is hoped, will aid materially in the development of data/information centers by providing efficient, accurate and rapid document retrieval systems for use by such centers.

RECENT DEVELOPMENTS IN DATA/INFORMATION CENTERS

A most interesting and promising event, which is bound to have far-reaching effects on data/information availability in the engineering and physical sciences has been the establishment of a National Standard Reference Data System by the Federal Council for Science and Technology.[12] Administered by the National Bureau of Standards, it will "provide critically evaluated data in the physical sciences on a national basis, centralizing a large part of the present data-compiling activities of a number of government agencies".

Actually, a decentralized national system is contemplated, with centers located in other government agencies, at universities, research institutes, and so forth. The data will be provided by scientists and engineers who are expert in their own fields, as Touloukian suggested.[2] Mechanization is expected to play a leading role in facilitating both data input and output. A number of specialized services are planned, including the publication data accession lists, correlation and prediction services, mathematical and statistical services, summary reviews and various data compilations on a subscription basis.

Much of this activity is a logical outgrowth of the pioneering done by the Office of Critical Table at the National Academy of Sciences-National Research Council.

SOME EXAMPLES OF DATA/INFORMATION CENTER ACTIVITIES

I may have already steered too closely to the topics assigned to other speakers at this Institute. Before concluding, however, I would like to describe briefly some of the activities of specialized data/information centers in engineering and physical sciences, taken from the publication "Specialized Science Information Services in the United States," published by the National Science Foundation in November, 1961, and therefore somewhat out-of-date.

1. Project 44 of the American Petroleum Institute compiles data on the physical and thermodynamic properties of hydrocarbons and related compounds. Project 48 handles data on sulfur-containing petroleum compounds, and Project 52 is concerned with highly purified nitrogen compounds found in petroleum.
2. The Chemical Kinetics Data Project at St. Lawrence University collects, correlates and critically evaluates all data on the rates of chemical reactions.
3. A research project of the Manufacturing Chemists' Association has the formidable task of compiling critical data on the properties of all known inorganic and organic substances, except the hydrocarbons and certain related compounds. This is quite an undertaking, considering that there are probably several million compounds involved!
4. Thermodynamic properties are available from Dr. Touloukian's Thermophys.cal Properties Research Center at Purdue, The Thermodynamic Studies Project of the U.S. Geological Survey, The Thermochemistry Section of the National Bureau of Standards, among many others.
5. The Nuclear Data Project of the U.S. Atomic Energy Commission provides data relating to nuclear structure.
6. The International Geophysical Year resulted in the establishment of World Data Centers for cosmic rays, geomagnetism, seismology and gravity, aurora, glaciology, oceanography, rockets and satellites, and solar activity.

A number of publications containing data or information contributed by scientists or culled from the available literature may be mentioned.

The *Handbook of Biological Data,* now published under the sponsorship of the Federation of American Societies for Experimental Biology, has been in existence for a number of years. It relies upon contributions of data from knowledgeable scientists and represents a cross section of biology in its data and information content.

Index Chemicus, a publication of the Institute for Scientific Information, newly surveys the available literature for information relating to synthesized chemical compounds and presents such information in a highly readable form.

Lastly, our own series of *Index-Handbooks of Cardiovascular Agents*[13] attempts to provide information from the world literature concerning the effects of chemical substances upon the cardiovascular system. It is a large-scale pilot plant project in a small and highly-restricted area of biomedicine. Over forty thousand papers have now been processed. It is hoped that this effort may perhaps provide a model for the development of data/information centers in the medical sciences based upon the improved document storage and retrieval service which the MEDLARS system promises. It is from the historical point-of-view, a logical descendant of the Chemical-Biological Coordination Center[14,15], which represented the first attempt at the development of a data/information facility dealing with the relationship between chemical structure and biological activity.

SUMMARY

The next important development in the Science Information complex will most probably be concerned with the solution of data/information availability problems. Certain faltering steps have already been made in this direction.

The present Institute will, it is hoped, shed some light on possible approaches to the setting up of such service facilities in the years to come.

BIBLIOGRAPHY

[1] N.B. Gove and K. Way, "The Data Compilation as Part of the Information Cycle," *J. Chem. Doc. 2* (1962), 179-181.

[2] Hearings before the Ad Hoc Subcommittee on a National Research Data Processing and Information Retrieval Center of the Committee on Education and Labor, House of Representatives, 88th Cong., 1st Sess. vol. 1 (1963) pp. 181, 183.

[3] *Ibid.,* p. 155.

[4] *Ibid,* p. 158.

[5] Science, Government and Information.

[6] J. C. Costello, Jr. and E. Wall, "The Engineers Joint Council Battelle Memorial In-

stitute Coordinate Indexing and Abstracting Training Course," *J. Chem. Doc. 4* (1964), 26–29.
[7] Science Information Notes *6* (1964), 1.
[8] *Ibid.* 5 (1963), 7–8.
[9] *Ibid.* 6 (1964), 12-13.
[10] *Ibid,* 5 (1963), 9.
[11] *Ibid.* 6 (1964), 9.
[12] *Ibid.* 5 (1963), 1–3.
[13] Isaac D. Welt, "Guide to the World Literature on Cardiovascular Agents." *Med. Doc. 5* (1961), 9–10.
[14] George A. Livingston and Isaac D. Welt, "Chemical Structures and Responses of Organisms to Applied Chemicals," *Adv. Doc. Libr. Sci. 2* (1957), 250–270.
[15] Isaac D. Welt, "Aspects of the CBCC Biology Code of Interest to Chemists," *J. Chem. Doc. 1* (1961), 19–21.
Presented before the Institute on Data/Information Availability of the American University Center for Technology and Administration, May 25, 1964.

DISCUSSION

FROM THE FLOOR: Can you give us an appraisal as to whether or not the courses which you are now promoting are designed to do the following:

1. Are we sufficiently impressing the student with the modus operandi of information services and the need to broaden his education by using them?
2. Are we training sufficient people to enter the field of data and information retrieval at the university?

DR. WELT: To start on an optimistic note, the chemists have, for the past several decades, developed courses in chemical literature on the undergraduate level for most of the students majoring in chemistry. There are a number of texts in this area and handbooks which give the fledgling chemist an introduction to the literature resources of his field. Some schools even have research projects in the chemical literature for their graduate students which involve searching the available collection in order to find specific answers to problems which have been posed. I don't know of similar courses in other fields, such as physics or biology. In medicine, the problem is probably most acute. Here the need for up-to-date information on the part of the practitioner is too obvious to be emphasized. It is literally a matter of life or death. As freshmen, they usually receive a short lecture by the medical librarian on the use of the medical library facilities at that particular school. It is agreed that we are not doing an adequate job in training scientists in the use of the literature or making them aware of the availability of vast storehouses of data which may prevent them from "rediscovering the wheel" once again.

Training of information scientists is now becoming possible. I am associated at the present time with both the program at the American University as well as that of the Graduate School of Library Science at the Drexel Institute of Technology. The American University has been offering courses in this field, such as, "Types and Uses of Scientific and Technical Information," "Concepts of Editing," "Machine Systems," etc., as part of its program in the Technology of Management within the Center for Technology and Administration. The Drexel program is, at the present time, offering the Master's degree in Information Sciences. Courses such as "Acquisition and File Organization," "Scientific and Technical Abstracting and Indexing," "Hardware Systems" and so forth are offered at Western Reserve, Lehigh, Rutgers, and so on. Special librarians can profit by being exposed to such course offerings. There are many prospective candidates who possess backgrounds in the humanities and social sciences who might wish to enter the field of Information Science. Those who are highly motivated can pick up a great deal of subject matter background on the job, but this is not the most efficient method. Perhaps the science department ought to develop special courses, without the usual laboratory work, for such students.

FROM THE FLOOR: You described the document retrieval and information retrieval processes very clearly. In your estimation, what are some of the problems which confront the information field? How can we advance the process of information retrieval? Not, "how do we do it" necessarily, but the broader, overall problems involved?

DR. WELT: First and foremost, there is the question of adequately well-trained personnel. As I have said, this type of work represents what is probably the most highly complex activity the scientist is capable of. Extracting meaningful and useful information from other people's published work is not an easy task. In fact, as the laboratory itself becomes more automated, a large number of tasks which hitherto had occupied the scientist's time and energy can increasingly be delegated to technicians. The scientist then, ought to spend more of his time as a communicator, as a reviewer, as a teacher, as a monitor of the ever-increasing tide of publications. If you happen to be a member of an "invisble college" of several dozen workers in a highly specialized esoteric field, you have a particular obligation to aid communication.

As Dr. Touloukian has pointed out, part-time abstractors, indexers, and reviewers are valuable members of the information-storage and retrieval team. I know of at least one firm where the information people have gotten management to insist that every bench scientist spend one afternoon per week extracting information from the literature pertinent to the company's operations. This is one way of obtaining information personnel in a tight market.

Critical reviews are of particular importance in introducing scientists to new fields of research. Such reviews are best written by experts in their own areas. There is no remuneration for such important contributions, however. For example, if you are a pharmacologist and an expert on antihistamines, for example, you may spend as much as a month or two writing up a review with five or six hundred references. It has to be done as a labor of love.

I mentioned the *Handbooks of Biological Data* earlier. Their editorial office collects data from the files of individual scientists. Such data are published without evaluation or critical review. This has to be so, for reviewing of data is a very expensive process indeed–much more expensive than simple document storage and retrieval.

Permuted title indexes, table of contents publications are excellent media for "current awareness." However, Mel Voigt's studies of the information requirements of a representative group of Scandinavian scientists point out two other basic needs. Retrospective search is most efficiently handled by abstracting and indexing publications and the review articles which I've just been discussing. The third problem, that of "providing specific answers to specific questions" is largely unsolved. What I am talking about can be illustrated by the following hypothetical questions: "What is the effect of drug A on a patient with symptom B and a medical history of disease C? What is the coefficient of expansion of a new beryllium alloy? What are the physical properties expected of a chemical compound with a particular structural configuration?" Also, it is exceedingly difficult to obtain information on methodology unless you know the name of the man who developed the method. In this case, the Science Citation Index may lead you to the document. Limitations of time prevent me from further elaboration upon this question which is of crucial importance, it seems to me. Where are we going?

FROM THE FLOOR: Are you aware of any specific Technical Information Centers operating in the biomedical field and if so, where are they located?

DR. WELT: I should like to refer this question to Dr. Kelsey.

DR. KELSEY: I don't think that I can answer that question because it is too broad. Did you have a more specific question in mind?

FROM THE FLOOR: Yes. Take the field of neurophysiology for example. Have there been any specialized centers set up in this field? What about biomedical engineering?

DR. KELSEY: Not formally as such. There are a number of special groups in the country that are working in these areas and they entertain questions. I think that the best resource we have is the National Referral Center which has been set up at the Library of Congress. It is intended to do just precisely this–locate for you the group best qualified to answer any kind of question in a sharply defined area.

DR. WELT: I understand that Dr. Thorner at the Drexel Institute of Technology in Philadelphia is assembling the literature in the field of biomedical engineering as part of his program in that area and as an aid to his teaching duties.

STORAGE AND RETRIEVAL OF CHEMICAL AND BIOLOGICAL DATA

F. ELLIS KELSEY, PH.D.
Public Health Service
U. S. Department of Health, Education and Welfare

Since the beginning of this century, there has been an increasing effort to relate chemical structure to biological activity. This relationship is a favorite subject of seminars and other academic discussions. The effort had its origins with Paul Ehrlich, whose triumph was made possible by a straightening out of certain long-standing errors in chemical structure. In other words, when the chemical information was corrected, it became possible to derive new theories and hypotheses relating chemical structure to biological action. The consequences of this strategy have been demonstrated amply in more recent times.

Today chemical structure information is well understood, highly codified, quite formal, and apparently correct. Biological information is not so easily classifiable, but there are certain groups or families of drugs which have characteristic biological activities, more or less accurately predictable. We know, for instance, that chemicals that dilate the pupil are quite apt to cause dry mouth, suppress gastric secretion, raise body temperature, and drive you mad. This is one "family" of chemicals.

Members of another family, the antibiotics, are likely to have the commmon property of causing bone-marrow depression or agranulocytosis. The family of analgesic drugs immediately suggests the possibility of euphoria and addiction. So, clearly there are grounds for assuming a pattern to biological activities, even though these are not as formalized as is chemical structure information.

In the few commercially oriented laboratories which have taken the first steps toward use of computers for coordinating chemical and biological data, the savings of expensive research manpower have been tremendous. But the development of correlations not otherwise possible promises even greater benefits.

For example, a given pharmaceutical company may have as many as fifty thousand compounds in its house file, compounds on which it has proprietary interests and patent rights, compounds which it is interested in developing and possibly marketing as drugs. At the same time, that company may have as many as fifty different screening tests to identify biological properties of chemicals. Thus you can see there are two and one-half million possible tests for this store of compounds.

The science information handling group at one large company claims that savings from elimination of unwitting duplication in its own laboratories amount to more than the cost of the entire information-handling system. Another company claims that it can automatically retrieve data of a sort that they could not possibly retrieve in their previous manual systems.

In any system considerations, there must be a clear appreciation of the difference between document handling and information handling. For example, we have heard today that Adrenalin, when injected intravenously into the rat, increases the blood pressure. This is not always true. A most important fact about Adrenalin is that, under certain odd situations, its intravenous injection brings the blood pressure down. This observation, made under very special situations, has led to remarkable improvements in the design and introduction of drugs to treat man in shock. Such exceptional situations tell us that we are a long way indeed from handling biological information in any comprehensive way. I was quoted earlier as saying that ultimately we should strive to retrieve information rather than documents, and I really believe this, but I shall also quote from the rest of the same paragraph in which I said, "realistically, this is many years in the future".

Another point about information in documents comes up when a scientist, having done his bench work, writes his research report. First, he collects the data, calculates them and assembles them into tables. Then he writes up the interpretation of such data as he choses to present. Almost invariably the man who collects data doesn't trust them. He knows what is likely to be wrong with them. He looks askance at them. But also, almost always he who collects data and writes interpretations of them is deeply in love with his interpretation. Now, this situation is reversed when the paper is read. One tends to take the facts and figures reported in tables as coming directly from the Mountain and the interpretation as being something rather less than that.

An information system which retrieves such data, that are not really trusted by the man who compiles or collected them, is in for trouble.

Finally, there is a necessary distinction that must be made among the people who use information. On the one hand, there are the research scientists; on the other, the practitioners, such as engineers or physicians. An original report on scientific work is looked at quite differently by a research scientist and by a physician. The physician wants to know, for example, if the blood-pressure change in a rat also occurs in people. That is not the kind of information a scientist looks for when he studies data and their interpretation. Under what circumstances were the data obtained? What were the details of the experiment? What was the author's name? Where did he get his schooling? Do I know him or do I know somebody who knows him? Have I met him? What journals is he publishing in? Is it a good journal? Does he write precisely?

To return to the distinctions among users, I think there are identifiable differences. You can't give high school teachers or housewives the kind of scientific information that is required by a research scientist. The information has to be processed; there have to be judgments, and there has to be compromise. But I am not in favor of any more compromise than we really have to have. So, with these caveats about documents and information, I will go back to the subject of my presentation.

Suppose we have a computerized system wherein had been placed, in some magic way, all of the solid chemical information and all of the available biological information, with all of its qualifications. What good is it? If you try to anticipate the kinds of questions that you would ask of such a system, I think you can define the system itself more accurately than in any other way.

A most important question is, "Give me all of the publications which deal with compound X". First, if you are interested in research, what are other people doing with this same chemical? What has been done? You may wish to look at them all. But, for some chemicals, there are too many references. So you put a few more restrictive limits on the question and say, "Give me all of the publications dealing with compound X where there are some animal studies reported of some sort or another; or some clinical studies; or studies with rats; or studies with pregnant animals; or studies with pregnant women; or where there are reports on the effects on the bone marrow". All you get is a list, but this list is sometimes more valuable than the "information" that you might retrieve from such a system.

Another type of question which you might ask is, "Give me the names and structural formulas of all the chemical compounds which dilate the pupil and which cause sweating". This question would eliminate most compounds because most of those which dilate the pupil cause a drying-up of sweat. But there are some strange pharmacological facts which, because of their strangeness, often lead to new thinking. Another type of question might be: "Give me references to the literature relating to articles which discuss compounds like X, those which do the same kind of things X does". Now, this one may be tougher to answer, and yet this is where the big rewards are. If you are searching for chemicals which are better explosives, or better drugs, or better plastics, you want to look at the families of chemicals which do these things, and deduce a working hypothesis which will let you dream up a chemical which might have better action. This, then, is the difference between a specific search of the file about a specific chemical, and a generic search about chemicals which are related in one way or another in which you specify, this ring structure, or this side chain. You want to retrieve the names of chemicals which have these things in common, generically related group of chemicals.

Virtually all of the work in this area has been done by fragmentation codes, by grouping chemicals around the benzene ring, for example. These are not unique designations nor are they unambiguous designations. It is desirable to have a symbol for a chemical which can be machined, which is unique, and for which there is only one symbolization possible. All of the components of such a system have been worked on and there is a great array of possibilities for providing the needed resource. The goal is to go from a two-dimensional chemical structure to a machinable language which can be searched for compounds with stated substructural characteristics. The output should be the two-dimensional chemical structure of that compound.

The American Chemical Society is well advanced in this work. The aim is to convert all chemical structures to computer language and files which can be searched both for individual compounds and for structurally related compounds in any unpredetermined fashion, within the next two, three, or four years.

The original step–that of converting a two-dimensional structure to machinable language–started ten years ago with notation systems whereby the chemical structure was defined by a series of letters and numbers, the so-called line notation. The difficulty has been that the notation, where B, for example, stands for a benzene ring, cannot easily be searched for a component of a benzene ring. It has been necessary to develop matrix tables where all of the atoms and bonds are shown in their connectional relationships. This requires a large number of bits of information, difficult to store. You can also go from a line notation to an expanded table by machine and search the expanded matrix table for such substructural characteristics as you may choose. It is possible to write a program to go from an expanded matrix into a notation system, a series of letters or characters, and there is considerable advantage to being able to order a file by line notation for economy of storage.

One can use empirical formulas in this way, and yet you can't search such formulas. An empirical formula for a chemical compound may be unique but this is not often the case. In fact, on the average every empirical formula involves four different chemicals. The average range is between one and eight hundred. This is still another way of ordering a file.

Since there are some 2,500,000–3,000,000 chemical compounds which are known now, the ordering of these files is a perplexing task.

Finally, the most promising way to provide a store of addressable information is by numbers arbitrarily assigned so that every chemical compound, the structure of which we have specific knowledge, has a seven-digit number which is unique for that compound. The number carries no information other than an address to the information filed under that number. I feel confident that there will be established within the next two or three years a complete file of chemical structure information, with such a registry number for each structure.

Eighteen years ago, the National Research Council established the Chemical-Biological Coordination Center. The Center was primarily designed for the development of codes and notational schemes for the collection, storage, and dissemination of chemical and biological information. The first objective was to facilitate the study of relationships between chemical structures and biological activity. The second objective was to sponsor a screening program to collect further information about biological activities to fill information gaps. Lesser objectives were to prepare and publish reviews and sponsor symposia on the effects of chemical structure on various biological activities. The Center had a unique opportunity for coordinating the results of experimentation and fulfilling requests for specific information.

The Center was discontinued in 1957 because of an inability to attract adequate and stable financial support. This was due largely to the failure to limit objectives and scope of operations; they tried to do too much with the resources at hand.

Despite the misfiring of this Chemical-Biological Coordination Center, the central idea has persisted. CBCC was seriously understaffed and its equipment was primitive. It was ahead of its time. Subsequent development in electronic data processing equipment makes these objectives technically feasible, beyond doubt.

In summary, the hard core of chemical or biological knowledge is the two-dimensional representation of chemical structures. This knowledge is fixed, precise, and describable. It can be stored in a computer and it can be retrieved through generic searches for such formulas as may have specified substructural characteristics. When this capacity is teamed up with an analogous capacity for handling information about drugs, or plastics, or any other chemically based field, then research in that field can be more intelligently planned.

The translation of chemical structure information into the formal language which is required for computer use has been accomplished in a variety of ways. Computer programs for generic substructural searches have been written. The system as a whole is feasible, and scientifically necessary. It is also going to be very expensive; we must now have detailed appraisal of the possible benefits and values that such a mammoth operation may be expected to provide.

DISCUSSION

DR. WELT: I should not have stuck my neck out on the Adrenalin question knowing that an author of textbooks in pharmacology was sitting beside me. It illustrates what Dr. Kelsey was saying about the "softness" of biological information. There isn't any data which cannot be further modified or extended. I should have said that Adrenalin increases the blood pressure of rats when injected intravenously under a variety of highly specific experimental conditions.

DR. KELSEY: I may not like your interpretation anyway. I want to read what the investigator said.

DR. WELT: The point you mentioned concerning "personal involvement" with one's own data intrigues me. Saul Herner reported on the question of "subject slanting" of abstracts at the ICSI meetings in 1958. Does your previous education affect the type of abstract you write, even of your own work? For example, if you're abstracting a pharmacological paper for *Chemical Abstracts,* you probably might not bother to spell out, in detail, the strain of laboratory rat which you were using. One does have the tendency of "falling in love" with one's own data, with your own brain children. There is a tendency then, I believe, towards personal involvement. You do not ordinarily stress negative results. Not that you necessarily want to "sweep them under the rug", you just don't get around to mentioning them in a short abstract. Furthermore if the indexer indexes your abstract, instead of going back to the original paper, everybody gets the impression that the work ran smoothly and that the paper consists of nothing but positive information. In fact, we have found in our own work, where we compare graphs and tables (blood-pressure curves, etc.) in the paper with what the author says he has found, there are discrepancies. So, what do you index? Do you index what the author said, or do you index what he has shown? This is where we run into trouble, because if we index what we think he has shown, then who are we to decide? For this reason we must have among our indexers, qualified subject matter specialists with a Ph.D. or M.D. degree and they are hard to come by.

Now the same thing applies to what you said, Dr. Kelsey, about anticipation of questions. How do you anticipate questions in a changing area of science with feverish activities going on? How could you anticipate these questions? It is a rough problem. One thing is certain, if you are not a scientist, you have no possible chance of anticipating questions. If the science information man himself represents a cross section of possible users, he has a fighting chance to anticipate questions. If he remembers the time when he himself used the literature or if he is a member of a team, who does research, and also does documentation or information handling, this is ideal. He is a processor of information as well as a user. And it takes one to know one.

Now, for the CBCC. I was for two years with the CBCC in charge of storage and retrieval of the medical and chemical drug area. We were ahead of our time (we hear this over and over again). Yet, I have attended a lot of documentation meetings where very little is known about the CBCC and its record. The CBCC developed approaches which are still valuable today. Furthermore, very little has been done in continuing this type of activity except, perhaps within the drug industry. Actually the Center was killed in 1957, during one of the government economy drives by unimaginative bureaucrats who didn't realize the importance of this type of activity (I wouldn't be surprised if there are still many of them around). We hadn't "sold" our program at all. It is true that it failed to limit its objectives. It tried to be "all things to all men" in order to solicit financial support. The late Dr. Milton C. Winternitz, the "godfather" of the Center, believed that all biology was indivisible, which is true to a great extent. We did do some research. I remember, for example, a positive correlation between antischistosomiasis compounds and those active in preventing the fouling of ships by barnacles. We had to extract and code pesticide information, information on chemicals which were used to kill lampreys in the Great Lakes, anticancer compounds, and all kinds of things.

Incidentally, the entire annual budget of the CBCC, if I remember correctly, was in the neighborhood of two hundred and twenty thousand dollars. We had about five or six Ph.D.'s on the staff and we just simply couldn't afford to do much more.

You are quite right to mention that the equipment was primitive. We didn't even have an IBM 101. We had two million IBM cards in a rotated file. Everything was done on the conventional sorter; no computers. Back in 1953 or 1954, these gadgets weren't available. Even if they had been available, we could not have afforded them. We spent some $25,000 a year renting IBM equipment. As far as the uniqueness of the services was concerned, I have in my files questions which we answered, many concerning basic research. I wouldn't place an estimate on the value of our answers. Those of you who might be interested in the chemical structure code which was developed and the biological code which followed may obtain copies of these from the Publications Office of the National Academy of Sciences. These were developed as a preliminary step towards a Data/Information Center dealing with the relations between chemical structure and biological activity. There is no reason why this work could not have continued if adequate staff and funds had been available.

DR. KELSEY: I would like to rebut. One thing I forgot to point out in the distinction between Information and Documents. Documents are permanent records. They last forever. It is a useful thing to go back fifty or a hundred or a thousand years and read documents. Information ages very fast and isn't current as soon as you get it. Secondly, I think probably the fundamental reasons the CBCC failed was that it tried to handle *information* and it was too soon. I think it still is. I think information *about* documents is about as far as we can go now.

DR. WELT: I disagree with that completely.

FROM THE FLOOR: Maybe you have answered my question with the last statement. It seems as though we have quite good techniques for acquiring, storing and retrieving documents. There is some good work going on among specialized groups on so-called critical analysis. They are coming up with a new document that is the latest word; this is very expensive and very limited in scope, I might add, and probably one hundredth of one percent of the knowledge that you cover in the entire collection. But then the problem in between, of sorting out the information, classifying it, storing it, retrieving it, as either numerical data or as very specifically oriented information on a subject, seems to be almost impossible. We have given it an awful lot of thought. Here you have a kind of fluid system based on your permanent documents, perhaps identified as critical information. Then there is this other fluid system of partially evaluated material. How to handle it?

We must have something that is continuously up-to-date. We can think of storing a lot of this material on magnetic tape. We can think of staffing our center with people who can keep some information at their fingertips by the old conventional means, but we don't have any mechanized way. This appears to really need greater emphasis.

DR. KELSEY: It just occurs to me that in this world we live in, the words you use sometimes connote a great deal more than is intended. But I can phrase it this way, documents represent facts; information represents opinion. Now, "opinion" is not a "good" word, as compared to "fact." This is another evidence that I find myself getting more and more discouraged about "information" handling systems. I seem to be searching for "bad" words to describe it and "good" words to describe documentation.

FROM THE FLOOR: In information retrieval there are many factors, primary factors, which prevent us from succeeding in retrieving information. What are these factors? There are also second-order factors, not as important as the first ones.

DR. WELT: May I just make one comment on that? If I were to have the choice of saying what is the main critical problem involving nonretrieval of documents, I'd say poor indexing by nonsubject matter people. No matter what kind of sources you have and what kind of scope notes, indexing can be no better than the training of the people who are doing the indexing. This is why *Chemical Abstracts* has a staff of permanent subject-matter qualified indexers, second to none in the world.

FROM THE FLOOR: All information is not in documents.

DR. WELT: Before you can get information I think you ought to have the documents available which contain it.

FROM THE FLOOR: Not all information comes from documents?

DR. WELT: That is quite true.

FROM THE FLOOR: Why do you have the pessimistic viewpoint of ever obtaining an information retrieval capability for many years in the future? Is there any reason for this?

DR. KELSEY: I think you have to explain the reasons why information retrieval is difficult before you can say we will solve difficult problems.

When we speak now about information retrieval, we are speaking about retrieval of factual knowledge other than bibliographical information. I think that the basic defect is that we don't have very much solid factual knowledge in biology. It is frequently said that when a student goes through medical school, half of what he learns will be proven wrong within five years. On the other hand, information concerning chemical structures is factual, solid, permanent, lasting information. So, we can code it and it will be the same tomorrow as it was yesterday. But this really isn't true about biological "facts". How do you manage this in an information-retrieval system?

DR. WELT: It may well be that chemical structures are permanent facts but what about chemical reactivity? I am sure most of us learned in high school that there were six inert gases that never reacted chemically. What has happened in the last three years?

DR. KELSEY: I think the system that we are now trying to use, to retrieve knowledge about documents, has certain obvious defects because of human errors, particularly indexing errors. This is also true about information retrieval. How do you record the information so that it really is recorded? The input into the system, if it is less than total, is only partial. Now we don't know what the total information is which is contained in a document. We do know that an important part of the information is the quality of the paper the document is written on. You tend to believe something if it is set up in good type and not to believe it if it is handwritten or typewritten. Now, this is important, and yet in our information-retrieval system we neglect these secondary things. They are not even recognized.

FROM THE FLOOR: Just a question to clear up in my own mind Dr. Kelsey's position. Do you believe that the Weinberg report indicated that a true technical information center cannot be achieved at all?

DR. KELSEY: That is the kind of information center that I think of as most suitable for the practicing physician. The practicing physician does not want, has not time to read, detailed scientific reports. He needs judgment, summaries, evaluations, and these should be as good, as reliable and as current as possible. This is digested information. The technical information centers, which are all of the things that the

Weinberg report described, are very useful. However, a good scientist likes to know what the opinions of other good scientists are about a field, but he won't necessarily believe it. It's just another thing to take into account. Review articles, for example, are important to scientists but they are not the be-all and end-all to information management for scientists.

DR. WELT: The question of communication between scientists and managers or administrators is another example of a lack of communication which I think I may have dwelled upon when I talked about the demise, the decline and fall of the CBCC. As Dr. Kelsey pointed out, we didn't sell it. Part of the selling bit is to communicate with managers in their own language. If you are way ahead of the game, it becomes exceedingly difficult. It it hadn't been for Einstein's letter to President Roosevelt we wouldn't have had the Manhattan project. We haven't learned enough about information storage and retrieval as yet to sell it properly.

FROM THE FLOOR: It seems to me that we have clarified our viewpoint somewhat but it would be well to pause a moment to talk about principles. I am sure they will differ with our requirements as they would differ with chemical, biological, or scientific or engineering or whatever the application. It would appear that we are concerned about a proper data base and in our experience, maintaining this data base is one of our greatest problems. For instance in the Navy, when they talk about a system, they are referring to a piece of hardware. When we talk about a system, we must also be concerned with the program that runs on that piece of hardware and so the term "system" gets to be a semantic problem. It has been stated that information was not necessarily factual. Now, this has been a problem to us and I wondered if you meant it just that way. We have noted that information may very well be a fact in a particular isolated situation. The problem that confronts us is to gather a lot of information or a lot of these bits and pieces that are facts unto themselves in isolated cases and then evaluate them. Just because we store and retrieve a document it doesn't necessarily follow that you give a great deal more credence to it just because it is a document. Yet, owing to its being a document, it is more likely to have a certain amount of evaluated facts. You talked about documents retaining value for a long time, perhaps for years. This is true. Now the facts are likely to have been evaluated originally. Because we use them later on to compare with some other document or information doesn't necessarily discredit the original material. We feed them into a data bank and later retrieve the bank. We have to keep our data source and update it. To convert all that we know now into a single data bank that you can start using is one thing. Equally important is to keep it updated so that we have as continuous inputs, bits and pieces of facts or documents. When we attempt to retrieve this, we must bring human judgment to bear in order to render a decision at the time of use. Because the minute the thing becomes a document and we put it into any sort of data base, somehow we tend to rely on that irrevocably just because it has been documented. It is the rendering of human judgment against this data base that has now become an accumulation of facts, facts that were valid in their own time that provides our problem. What we seem to find is while some of this documentation that we retrieve becomes outdated, we still want to compare it with the updated data because only bits and pieces are really outdated and you still have to compare the old with the new to render judgment at the present time.

DR. KELSEY: The *Encyclopaedia Britannica,* known to all of you, is a collection of facts. It used to be that you could look at the front and see what year it was published and at least have a good guess as to the reliability of the materials presented therein. Now it is no longer dated. You can't use it as you did formerly. You don't know where you are at. Secondly, when you speak of evaluated facts, true facts, it seems to me that a fact is a fact, and you can't evaluate a fact. It's a fact, and in this context there are but few such facts. It is a fact according to the knowledge available at the time. It may not be a fact tomorrow. Now this matter of continuously updating is nice theoretically but practically impossible. If you have a collection of information, each item has to be tagged by its context, in time and reliability, and this is not usually done. The boiling point is 67.3, this is a fact, and if you had all of the information about that fact it would be more useful, i.e. if it were accomplished by somebody who had a sound reputation, if it's corrected for atmospheric pressure, if it was done in pyrex, and so on. Tomorrow you may discover that all the ones that were done in glass are not any good.

DR. WELT: Systems versus hardware or systems and hardware. In the prevailing commercial world, hardware firms will sell you equipment with the supposition that you are going to build a system around it. This is the wrong way of doing it. If you have adequate, qualified competent systems engineers, they will first of all develop a model system and then utilize what hardware is available. This is exactly what happened in the MEDLARS Project. The Project started out with a contract to G.E., and General Electric accepted the contract with the supposition they would be able to sell G.E. equipment. Instead, they ended up with a Honeywell 800. This is as it should be. Hardware is part of a system, not the other way around. It must be part of a system. You have to bring together, wed, various software and hardware components, and so forth. As soon as we get more standardization in the hardware field the better it will be for all who are working in mechanized storage and retrieval. Concerning "dating" of data, there is always some kind of chronological tag identified with data attached to documents. As you record a citation, you always have the year of publication. Now, when you begin to remove data from within the published paper, you ought to tag each datum with the date on which the work was done. For example, if we now have instruments that can refine a particular constant to ten decimal places you want to know this. There is no figure that is more accurate than the instrument that is used to develop it. So, you should "date" your data when putting it into the "bank."

There is a question relating to the half-life of documents. The librarians have been concerned with this for many years as a result of storage problems. When do you start moving past volumes of the *Journal of the American Chemical Society* to the basement for lack of display space? There has been developed the concept of half life of information. For physics literature it is from two to five years. In other words, half of all the references to all the articles asked for were published in the last five years. Let me continue further. The 19th century was known as the golden age of organic chemistry in Germany. In our normal operations this old material is completely useless and you remove it from the reference shelves. After all we have better synthetic methods now with better yields, etc. Suddenly along come isotopes, and a need arises for synthesizing compounds labeled with carbon-14 in a specific portion of the molecule. It turns out that many of the old synthetic methods are the best available for these specific purposes. The newer methods are terribly efficient, but they would not bring the labeled carbon into the position on the molecule which you wanted. A rush to the old literature begins, especially if you can read German, and the people begin unearthing all these so-called obsolete or obsolescent volumes. So, you really can't tell when a document becomes obsolete or when a fact becomes obsolete. The fact will become obsolete of course, depending on how you define a fact. This is entirely a question of philosophy and there's no sense in going into that at present.

DATA-RETRIEVAL AND GROWTH POSSIBILITIES

CHARLES DEVORE
Office of Naval Research

There are three quotations which I think are particularly pertinent to the topic Data-Retrieval and Growth Possibilities. They are: (1) "What is past is prologue"; (2) "Learn from the past"; and (3) "Those who cannot remember the past are condemned to repeat it."

To demonstrate the applicability of the first and second quotation, let me remind you that digital computers, as such, are only about twenty years old. The first electronic computer, ENIAC, was developed under Army sponsorship at the Moore School of Electrical Engineering of the University of Pennsylvania, and put into operation by the Army about 1947. In 1944, Professor Aiken of Harvard developed the Mark I machine. This used electromechanical relays as primary elements in arithmetic, storage, transfer, and input-output. The Navy participated in that development which demonstrated, really, the fundamental, logical operations which have been involved in subsequent digital computers.

In 1945 the Office of Naval Research–or to be more exact, the Office of Research and Inventions, which is what we were called at that time–initiated research on "Project Whirlwind" at the Massachusetts Institute of Technology. Although that project was originally conceived as a simulator, using analogue techniques, it quickly developed into a program to use digital-computer techniques in military command and control.

The early research efforts were concentrated in two areas. First, the building of a high-speed digital computer with appropriate input-output channels to tie into high-speed communication lines and associated visual display devices, and second, development of concepts for using digital techniques for control of friendly aircraft and tracking and interception of enemy aircraft.

In the early 1950's the Air Force joined in the support of this project and the work was considerably accelerated. The SAGE system (Semiautomatic Ground Environment), evolved from that, and was the first real-time command and control system. Design and construction were based on the investigation which had already been completed. This research project, along with research on "Project Cornfield" at the University of Illinois under a three-service contract initiated by ONR, led to plans during 1954 for the development of the Navy Tactical Data System (NTDS), a digital system for communications, command, and control. It is now installed on many ships of the Fleet.

I would like to list some of the additional payoffs–in the aerospace technology, I should say spinoffs–from "Whirlwind," and the work which continued under Project Lincoln. (1) The development of advanced computer hardware, particularly magnetic-core storage devices, which have greatly improved the speed, capacity, and reliability of both military and commercial computers. (2) The achievement of reliable programs for tracking, control, and interception of aircraft. (3) Advanced programming languages, both for data processing and military control. (4) Improved display devices, which are useful both for control and intercept as well as for operational control and intelligence operations. (5) Accurate, dependable devices converting radar signals to digital pulses for insertion to digital computers. (6) Techniques of retrieval and display of information and means of control that are finding increasingly profitable application in industrial and commercial activities.* I return to the listing of the payoffs from "Whirlwind." (7) New techniques for preventive maintenance of digital computers. (8) The first digital control of machine tools carried out in connection with Project Whirlwind. (9) The training in the late 1940's and early 1950's of more than one hundred engineers and scientists in digital techniques. These men have dispersed to all parts of the country to form groups which have in turn made significant contributions to digital computer technology as well as to command and control.

Now, in anticipation of the question later, one might make a couple of points. It isn't claimed that the Office of Naval Research, the Navy, or even the Department of Defense is sponsoring all the research and development work in the general area of computers. I do claim, however, the illustration just used is representative of the commercial and the indus-

*As a sidelight at this point I would like to call your attention to an article which appeared in *Fortune* for April, 1964, on SABRE. This is American Airlines new $30 million real-time seat-reservation system, and the world's largest real-time commercial application. Perhaps like me you hadn't realized that more than eighty different actions are involved in making a seat reservation. The SABRE system contains more than one million instructions and the specifications for its programs fill five thick volumes. To quote from the *Fortune* article, "Without SAGE there would be no SABRE, at least not for a long time."

trial benefits derived directly from research and development programs sponsored by the government and primarily by the Department of Defense. These programs are carried on at universities or nonprofit organizations or within the government's own laboratories. Costly? Yes, they are costly. But how do you equate experience in development as well as operation of the machine against cost?

It is only logical that the Department of Defense should play the major role in such research and development work. As we all are aware, the Department of Defense budget accounts for more than fifty cents out of every dollar in the over-all Federal budget. So, naturally the Department of Defense has a real concern with helping to improve the availability of data and information.

Mr. Vance, the Deputy Secretary of Defense, stated in March of this year, "The cost and scope of the technical information requirements of the DOD are huge. It is estimated that at least two billion dollars out of our annual expenditures are invested in securing such data."

At this time, some definitions are in order. These, for the most part, come from a glossary which was prepared for the Federal Council of Science and Technology in order that the members of the council would attach the same meaning to certain terms that are sometimes used interchangeably but improperly. According to the glossary, data are defined as "symbolic representations of information"–for example, letters, numerals, or other characters in a document or the record of signals received from a sensing device. Information is defined as "the meaning assigned to data". This broad category includes engineering information, proprietary information, scientific information, and technical information. A document is a record of data or a concept in any form from which information can be derived. For example, a page containing data, a graphic representation, a tape recording, a book, or a technical report, is a document. This does not imply that a document is limited to just a technical report. Technical logistics and data (which I will be primarily concerned with and talk about in one of the systems) as defined by the Department of Defense include such items as "production engineering data, prints and drawings, documents such as standards and specifications, technical manuals, changes and modifications, inspection and testing procedures and performance and failure data". Now, if there is an overlap–or to use another currently popular word, interface–between technical data and technical information, you are quite right. In recognition of this fact of life, the Department of Defense in March of this year established a Department of Defense Council on Technical Data and Standardization Policy. This Council is co-chaired by the Assistant Secretary of Defense (Deputy Director of Research and Engineering), Dr. Fubini, and the Assistant Secretary of Defense (Installation and Logistics), Mr. Morris. Now, before returning to a specific topic, I must state that I agree with those who point out that we have no machines today that provide information retrieval. We do have systems that provide document retrieval, the largest of these being the Defense Documentation Center. Incidentally, DDC, as it is known, evolved from an ONR contract with the Library of Congress in 1947, which was just one year after ONR's establishment by Public Law.

Now, to return more directly to the topic of Data-Retrieval and Growth Possibilities. Once you have identified your problem, as in the case of engineering data, how do you go about developing a possible solution? Well, the approach and the solution involve both policy and technique. Let's consider a very current example, the proposed Department of Defense Engineering Data Retrieval System, "EDRS." This is a proposed system. Briefly, you might refer to EDRS or describe it as a DDC in the area of engineering data rather than in the area of scientific and technical documents. A group of five members of the Department of Defense chaired by a representative of the Defense Supply Agency, was assigned the task of developing this system. Their job was to evolve a plan for the installation of a system for the interchange of engineering data among the military services, DSA (the Defense Supply Agency), and industry to provide more efficient support of research, development, test and evaluation processes, production engineering and the logistics functions of procurement value engineering and standardization. Their objective was to establish an engineering data retrieval system which (1) can be implemented within a short time span and produce early benefits; (2) can be expanded to handle all engineering data appropriate to this interchange; (3) can be progressively refined to take full advantage of advanced techniques of mechanized data retrieval.

The approach taken by the project group was to examine the operation of existing systems for the interchange of data, determine the need in engineering-data-retrieval systems and the type of system needed and then to analyze the findings and develop them. The group was given ninety days to carry out their assigned task. During that time—this was not just a desk job—they visited and talked with engineers and scientists at some fourteen government and industrial activities. These are their analyses: (1) On the development of the DOD interchange system (although an over-all DOD mechanized system for the interchange of data does not exist today), the retrieval systems being operated by the individual services and industry may be used as building blocks for the development of such a system. In other words, no new system. (2) Concerning the need for an engineering-data-retrieval system, there are millions of drawings, standards, specifications, test results, characteristic descriptions, and other engineering data, for military weapons, equipment, and parts. These documents are spread throughout the files of the services and DSA with no comprehensive machinery for their interchange and reuse within and among government and industry activities. This situation has resulted (according to industry reports, Congressional testimony, and in-house studies), in redundant research and development, duplications of data already procured, excessive procurement costs, excessive data management costs, and the duplication of documentation by many contractors. There is, therefore, an urgent need for a DOD engineering-data-retrieval system for acquiring, classifying, storing, retrieving, distributing, and interchanging data for use in engineering and logistics. Whatever the cost necessary to do this job, the group stated that it will be saved many times over when such a system becomes operational and is fully utilized by the military services, DSA, and industry. (3) Concerning type of engineering data system needed, this will be a system through which an RDT&E or production engineer can look to one source for a given commodity and can obtain an item data package which will contain all the available data on that item. That is, the user would be able to retrieve all engineering data available on an item or group of items by rapid mechanized retrieval as opposed to searching for data from multiple sources as he must do today. The system plan for the EDRS provides for an engineering data file located at government and industrial laboratories which are engaged in research, development, test and evaluation, and production engineering. This file would also be made available to logistics activities engaged in procurement, standardization and value engineering. The file will contain a package of engineering data for each item in the EDRS. A data package will include item data sheets, drawings, specifications, standards, test reports, and other available data needed by the user. According to the proposal, the first year's selection of item data packages is estimated to total 250,000. This includes 44,000 item data packages for resistors, 68,000 for missile parts, 26,000 for capacitors, 62,000 for hardware, and 50,000 for bearings. These item data packages will be furnished to the user in the media of his choice. He has a choice of six; sixteen-millimeter microfilm cartridges, 16-mm microfilm reels, 35-mm microfilm reels, 35-mm aperture cards, microfiche or hard copy. In other words, a user doesn't have to set up a new facility to make use of this system's services. Incidentally, a microfilm reel has a capacity of approximately 2,000 16-mm size pages of documentation.

The engineering data file itself is to be arranged or structured to permit rapid data retrieval, utilizing the mechanized retrieval equipment at the using facility. An index will permit entry into the file by alphabetically listed descriptors and the major characteristics of an item so that the user may retrieve the complete engineering data package on the item or on specific parts of that package. Cross-reference indexes will permit data retrieval when a part number, drawing number, or Federal stock number is known.

Here is an example of the indexing system. To begin with, there will be an alphabetical descriptor system, i.e., "bearings," "capacitors," and "resistors," etc. Then there will be an alphabetical subdescriptor system. For example, resistors, fixed. Next, there will be an alphabetical subsubdescriptor listing, thus, resistors, fixed, wire-wound. The major characteristic of the item will then follow: "resistors, fixed, wire-wound, one to one hundred ohms". The file would indicate, by a numbering system, the number for the various media; the microfiche, the aperture card, the cartridge, whatever is needed. There will also be cross-indexing. For instance, the entry "condensers" will state that "capacitors" is to be preferred and will indicate, "*see* capacitors".

As is the case for other data-retrieval systems, EDRS will be progressively improved and expanded, not only to include additional items, but also to take advantage of the advanced techniques of mechanized data retrieval to improve the systems operation.

Concerning cost effectiveness, the group estimated that in two areas alone–"engineering search time" and "item entry control"–there is potential cost-saving of thirteen dollars for every dollar invested. In their study they found an average of about 24 percent of the engineer's worktime is now spent in locating data. That is not going to be eliminated, but it can be reduced to about 18 percent through the use of EDRS. And incidentally, 95 percent of the engineers they interviewed believed that the EDRS was urgently needed and would provide them with a most valuable tool.

Now, looking to the future, what does one see? A major national program of research on advanced computer systems was recently initiated at the Massachusetts Institute of Technology, as a result of a contract between MIT and the Office of Naval Research acting on behalf of the Advanced Research Projects Agency. This contract was under the technical supervision of the Information Systems Branch of ONR and was given the name "Project MAC". The identification given this project is an *acronym* having two meanings. One is "Machine-Aided Cognition". The other is "Multiple-Access Computer". This project was directed by Professor Robert Fano and it was and still is intended to be the initial phase of a national effort that is expected to involve an increasing number of universities and research centers.

The central part of Project MAC is an experimental investigation of ways in which computers can more effectively aid people in their creative work, whether that work is to be scientific research, education, engineering design, or management. So, an essential part of the project is the continuous evolution of a computer system easily and independently accessible to a large number of people and truly responsive to their individual needs. Equally essential is the development and implementation of languages that are more suitable for close man-machine interaction and capable of evolving with the conceptual structure of the field in which they are used. In other words, it's not only necessary that the user have access to the system at a time and place through a device which is convenient to him, but it is also necessary that he be able to interact with the system in a language that suits him as a human being and is appropriate to the situation that he wants to investigate. Meeting this language objective is really the most difficult part of the task undertaken by Project MAC.

There has been much discussion concerning the idea of "talking with machines". I think the opinion at the moment is that this is not very feasible or desirable. The advantage of talking with a human being is that, although you state one thing, he can reply that isn't what he really meant to say and so the dialogue goes on until you know exactly what is on his mind. A machine can't do that. You must be precise or you will receive an incorrect answer.

Finally, Project MAC fosters and supports basic research on the representation, analysis, and synthesis of complex logical processes in order to give a deeper and broader foundation to the entire field of information processes. The emphasis of Project MAC, then, is to place the logical power of computers at the service of people where, when and in the amount wanted, somewhat in the same manner as electrical power is distributed. Professor Fano is credited properly with the term "Computer Utility," which would be similar to the more familiar telephone, electric, and gas utilities.

Using that analogue, we might say that the present situation with computers is similar to that of mechanical power just after the invention of the steam engine. The MAC system is currently based on an IBM 7094 installation, employed around the clock, seven days a week, for a total of 21 eight-hour shifts per week. It is operated in the "time-sharing mode", except for short periods, during which it is made available for uses not now compatible. The IBM 7094 central processor has been modified to operate with two banks of core memory rather than with one, each consisting of 32,000 computer words. It is also modified to provide facilities for memory protection and relocation.

One of the memory banks is available to the user's program, and the other is reserved for the supervisory program of the "time-sharing system". The central processor, the 7094, is equipped with six data channels which are, in effect, small special-purpose computers. Two of the data channels are used as interfaces to magnetic tapes, printers, card readers, and card punchers. A third data channel provides direct data connection to terminals that require high-rate transfer of data; for example, they have a nearby display console developed by the M.I.T. Electronics Systems Laboratory for what is known as "Computer Aided Design", a project supported by the Air Force. Each of the next two data channels provides communication with a disk file and with a drum. Each disk file can store up to 9 million computer words and each drum up to 185,000. The time required to transfer 32,000 words in or out of core memory is approximately two seconds for the disk file and one second for the drum. The two disk files are used for the user's private files of data and programs as well as public programs. The two drums are used for temporary storage of active programs. Finally, a transmission control unit (which is a stored program computer) serves as an interface between the six data channels and up to 112 communication terminals. The primary terminals of the MAC system are forty Model 35 teletype machines, capable of 100 words per minute operation. Two of these are located at Lincoln Laboratories, in nearby Lexington, and the rest are in various offices, laboratories, and homes on the M.I.T. campus. Each of these can dial the MAC computer installation directly, going through the M.I.T. private branch exchange. The number of telephone lines connected to the installation limits the number of simultaneous users of the MAC computer installation to twenty-four. These teletypes are sufficiently fast insofar as the user is concerned but they are, of course, very slow for the computer.

Long Distance Teletype access is by means of IBM Selectric typewriters. The system will be connected to the TWX and Telex networks which are operated respectively by AT&T and Western Union. Experiments are planned in cooperation with a number of universities to provide experience with long-distance operation of time-sharing systems. In addition, such connections will make it possible to demonstrate the operation of the system for any terminal of the two networks. The TWX terminal, for example, includes approximately 65,000 teletypes, and the Telex network provides access from terminals in Europe as well as in the United States. Looking toward the future is the possibility of having scientists abroad and in this country discussing their problems, working them out mutually on the computer.

The operating program of the MAC computer system is called the "Compatible Time Sharing System", CTSS, which was previously developed by the MIT computation center with the support of ONR and NSF. This is again, an evolving system. Its first public demonstration took place in 1961. CTSS includes executive, scheduling, debugging, assembler, compiler, and input/output facility. The program languages presently available on the system are COMIT, FAP, FORTRAN, LISP, MAD, SLIP, a limited version of ALGOL, and two problem oriented languages for civil engineering, one called "COGO" and the other "STRESS."

In a typical case, the user first logs in, giving his identification. He can then type in a subroutine, perhaps using the "MAD" language, and then call for a printout of his input, edit to correct errors, or call for a compilation. The resulting binary program, possibly with other programs already compiled, can then be loaded and run. If the run is unsuccessful, the user can request post-mortem data to assist in locating the fault. If necessary, the user can examine the contents of machine registers, correct the source program, recompile it and so forth, perhaps several times. When he is ready to terminate his session, he logs out, at which time he receives accounting data indicating how much actual computer time was used.

As we are all aware, new computer installations are constantly being planned. Even though the 7094 was the largest ever built, the 7094 was not designed to meet the needs of a multiple-access system. The two equipment characteristics which appear to be most important are a much larger primary memory system, (possibly as large as one million words), and a multiprocessor configuration, (one in which the primary memory consists of several independent units), both of which can be directly addressed by several independent processes.

Of rather unique interest is a computer aided program known as "Sketch Pad". By means of this, an engineer can directly communicate with a computer by drawing on a cathode-ray tube utilizing a light pen that resembles a small flashlight. For instance, the engineer might sketch the design of a component part on the face of the tube. The computer will then straighten the lines and remake the drawing to a standard size. IF the engineer so desires, specifications for standard subassemblies of the component, such as bearings, etc., can be stored in the computer and added to the drawing. Working on the visual display, the engineer may then modify his drawings as he proceeds. Later he can test the part by indicating where loads should be applied and the computer can calculate and display information on deformation or failure. Eventually, M.I.T. researchers say, when the designer has finished, the computer will be able to produce a tape to control a machine tool actually producing the part.

In closing, I would like to bring you back to those first two quotations, "What Is Past Is Prologue", but "We Can Learn from the Past". If we don't, then we are in danger of repeating it.

PART II

THE SCIENCE OF MANAGEMENT AND DATA/INFORMATION

RELATIONSHIP BETWEEN AVAILABILITY OF DATA AND SIGNIFICANT TECHNOLOGY ADVANCES

DR. C. S. DRAPER
Massachusetts Institute of Technology
Cambridge, Massachusetts

In this busy world there is little time for contemplation and deciding upon the state of one's own particular progress with respect to the broader aspects of significant technological advances and their dependence upon prior work. It is even more difficult to plan so that one is always in the "mainstream" of activity, although there are various things that can be done to insure a "front seat in the bus". Being associated with one of the larger centers of technological learning for some thirty-five years has undoubtedly meant for me a closer awareness of our modern "Explosion of Knowledge" than might otherwise have been the case. Furthermore, the Instrumentation Laboratory within my Department (Aeronautics and Astronautics) at M.I.T. has been a "beehive" attracting competent minds to work on frontier research and development. That we have made good use of our opportunities, I leave for others to say. Beyond doubt we have extended our minds and energies to cover many fields. Perhaps out of the resulting experiences a definitive concept of management has evolved. Let us examine results to see if this is actually the fact.

Let us talk about putting "men with ideas" to work on challenging programs, in terms of operations by the Instrumentation Laboratory of M.I.T. which is the heart of research and development for my Department of Aeronautics and Astronautics. The technical areas covered during the past thirty years include aeronautical power plants, autopilots, fire-control devices, gun sights, and lately, navigational systems for ships and ballistic missiles. Specifically, the Laboratory has designed the guidance package for *Polaris,* for the Titan missile, for the Thor missile, and is now working on guidance for the Apollo manned round trip to the moon. In each case, our job has been to conceive, design, build the first model, check out the engineering concepts by tests, produce manufacturing information, and supply documentation. Our job isn't done until an over-all system is in successful use. In the case of Apollo this means use on an actual trip to the moon and back.

The type of operation described means that we always assume complete responsibility for the entire job to be done. We do not issue large subcontracts ourselves, although we deal with many subcontractors who are part of the over-all production arrangement set up by the government. On the financial side, the Laboratory is doing business at the rate of some $40 to $42 million a year. Our customers include many government agencies but most of the funding is received from the Air Force, from NASA, and from the Navy. Between the Department and the Laboratory, I have the responsibility–not credit–for somewhere around 2,200-2,500 people who, in association with the academic department, are expending funds that represent some $43 million a year. I need not add that the Laboratory is now an operation of considerable complexity, although I remember very well in the early days, with only myself and two or three other people worked together on rather simple devices. Certain highlights stand out–for instance, back in 1926 infrared signaling sensors worked well, although the results were regarded as of little importance because something was just coming along that depended on short radio waves, to become radar a little later. I remember being at the Naval Laboratory for demonstrations that were overshadowed by this development.

It is reasonable to expect that if you contribute technical achievements you should be able to realize some financial return for your efforts. I admit that I personally haven't done very well in this area. I like to think one reason for this is that I never tried very hard for money because I have enjoyed technical jobs so much that it always seemed better to go ahead on something new, than to stop and fight about how much I could get in the way of reward for what had already been done. This is not quite as bad as it sounds because of the considerable fun in working in an always pioneering laboratory that has been quite successful, and has even been awarded a few contracts that some people thought should go to industry. I would like to remark here that, although the laboratory conceived and initiated the many projects and successfully completed the required jobs, it has been American industry that received orders in billions of dollars for the resulting products. Over a period of thirty-five years, always playing a "sudden death" game with no reserves, with never more than minimum resources, we have remained alive and made significant contributions to pioneering developments of technology. The rules under which we operate say that if we do not have a contract to cover the next payroll, I've got to give out dismissal notices to employees because the Institute provides no funds to "tide over" between contracts. Whatever new proposals are produced have got to be generated largely "under the table". This is not too difficult because there is a lag of a few days, or even weeks, in the bookkeeping system. With good luck, we've often been able to find something new before this "buffer" period ran out. This means by and large that the environment in which I have worked has been somewhat abnormal. I would say that out of the resulting experiences, I have learned by hard knocks that wisdom must be used to supplement rules as they may be appplied to whatever tasks are involved in each situation. There are no regulations that say that if you do this or that you'll be successful. Every situtation is a separate case in which many factors must be carefully weighed in planning courses of action. My goal has never been to build up an organization, a lot of facilities or something with stability for the future. Rather, the objective has always been the successful completion of accepted projects. The people of the Laboratory have the usual protection provided by the rules of educational institutions, but of even greater importance is the enhanced reputation and capability that come from working with a group of able people in an atmosphere of effective creativity. As it has turned out, many persons with experience in the Laboratory have later gone on to careers of distinction in a variety of fields. A good many small companies have been started by persons who have "spun off" from the Laboratory.

Information and Data play essential parts in modern living. I have just completed three weeks of almost continuous travel during which I've been engaged in examining the impact of information and data in industry, in the Air Force, in the Navy, and to a certain extent in the Department of Commerce. For instance, the whole activity at Fort Ord is leaning away from the traditional processes of field testing and toward the collection of data and making the derived information available to the Army for use in its planning of operational procedures. This is a relatively new kind of exercise which is assuming always greater interest and importance. I'm very familiar with the data collection that goes on in missile projects, activities in which such great expense is involved that it is essential to collect all possible information that can be obtained on the performance of each missile. This example is only one illustration to show that the collection of data is an essential part of modern engineering. Most of data-collection work involving military missiles is for the purpose of advancing missile technology, not for increasing the over-all store of fundamental human knowledge.

Data are essential for many purposes, among which are improvement of particular products, testing existing performance, and development of background information for further technological advances. When a sudden change in technology occurs, something new is started which often means that ideas and plans are abundant but that not very much sound information based on the data will be available until some future time.

The Wright brothers and their invention of the airplane illustrate this point. Some data on the concepts of flight were available to the Wright brothers before their work began, but these resources of knowledge were so meager that special experiments had to be carried out before the first airplane could be designed. Some of the aerodynamic information on the record was not only misleading but was actually incorrect. Thus we see that in the Wright brothers' work, available data played no more than a small role in getting them started toward successful manned flight. This is but one example of pioneering efforts in which someone must have the imagination, initiative, and willingness to take risks, coupled with an effective knowledge of physical principles. Intuition also plays a strong role in activities of this kind because if you are considering something really new logical answers can very seldom be derived from data at hand. Information must always be supplemented by inspiration.

Another example may be drawn from the discovery of high-energy particles that led to today's tremendous nuclear technology. The original investigations of these particles were not based upon a great array of information. As a matter of fact, the data were originally only a few streaks on photographic plates. It wasn't the availability of data that led to the development of "nuclear engineering" because the whole pattern did not depend upon a great mass of data, but involved new theories and concepts that were greatly different from accepted ideas. No amount of information, in terms of data alone, would have helped very much. You had to have an understanding of quantum theory and a notion of the way in which you could investigate particles of extraordinarily high energy levels. The examples cited suggest that at the genesis of new concepts, the automobile and the telephone are illustrations; the initial growth of useful fields is very much determined by the creativity and perseverance of human beings in applying new ideas. Transistors represent another good case illustrating the path of innovation. The phenomena of what happens in a semiconductor with bouncing electrons, followed by the controlled transfer of these electrons from one place to another, was something that had to be theorized and proven out. I happen to have received my doctor's degree in 1938 in the same class with Bill Shockley. Dr. Shockley is, of course, one of the persons who received the Nobel prize for the concept that led to today's transistor technology. There were some data to back up the concept involved, but taking it by and large it was the inspiration, the sheer application of mental power–thinking, not a whole lot of data or information–that laid the foundations for the great transistor technology of today.

Circumstances are different when an established technology such as that of present-day airplanes is considered. In a situation of this kind further technological advances come largely from information developed from great collections of data from carefully planned systematic experiments. Stimulating objectives are needed for motivation, while creativity is still an essential ingredient of progress, but significant advances in well-developed areas of technology must come from the availability of great amounts of data. In summary, I say that in the conceptual, the creative, the beginnings of a new technology, it is human ability, basic knowledge, and the flashes of genius that get things started. Once a sound foundation is provided, it becomes essential that adequate data be properly collected, processed, evaluated, and applied to technological advances. Advances of this kind depend upon the availability of comprehensive data that must be collected in a systematic fashion if they are to adequately describe the complex situations of modern engineering. You must have a complete pattern of available data if progress is to be maintained under the conditions of today.

As I have already mentioned, there is a whole spectrum of advances that you may obtain from very little data because of the extraordinary contributions from creative individuals. The airplane and its early development is a good example of this fact. Not so many years ago, pilots took planes up and made experiments with results described by data from readings of a few instruments recorded with pencils and kneepads. The jottings on those pieces of paper were the available data from which conclusions were drawn as to what should be done to realize the next steps toward better aircraft. Some years later in time, instead of jotting down numbers on a pad, movie cameras were used to take pictures of the instruments with data taken from the frames. Motion-picture films have now been largely replaced by magnetic tape recorders because of greatly increased capacity for data and easier processing for evaluation and application of results. The development of many devices for sensing, transmitting, processing and evaluation of data has led to an instrumentation business that today is surging ahead to provide better means for collecting the data that lead to progress in technology, industry and business.

I was aware that instruments were going to be important back in the 1930's. I've written a couple of books on instrument engineering in addition to a number of papers on this subject. I also conceived, developed, and taught instrumentation courses in days when there were only a few schools offering education in this field. What we called instrumentation was made up of various areas including measurement, stabilization, control, and guidance. I predicted some thirty years ago that the instrument business was going to be tremendous and events have certainly proven this opinion to be correct. I've forgotten how big the instrumentation industry is today but each year it certainly is a good many hundreds of millions of dollars, perhaps even billions. All over the world you see much expensive recording, receiving, and transmitting equipment in laboratories, field stations and plants concerned with routine operations and pioneering projects.

One of our most useful ways of obtaining aeronautical and astronautical data depends upon telemetry, or automatic transmission of information from flight vehicles to the ground. With the development of digital computers, our capabilities for acquiring, processing, and applying data were expanded in spectacular ways. We now control manned or unmanned satellites from information processed on the ground and transmitted back to space. In the technology of today, telemetry providing operation of this kind is a routine matter. I remember back in the early 30's that we carried out tests on pioneering models of the radiosonde, a little device sent aloft by means of a balloon to automatically contact earth stations with radio signals representing pressure, temperature, humidity, and other quantities. When the first units were built, they created quite a sensation since they would work while attached to airplanes in addition to being useful in balloons. A lot of people shook their heads at this because it was a sharp break with tradition and there were questions as to whether or not telemetry would be of any real use. Today radiosondes are the basis for a large business with hundreds of units sent aloft each day. The point to be noted is that the collection of information has received a strong shot in the arm by developments that have largely eliminated distance as a difficulty for the collection and use of data. This means, of course, that much data is being made available on a continuous basis in real time for many complex operations which depend completely upon information for the control of successful missions. With the essential data available, the next steps toward technological advances rest entirely on processing, evaluating, and understanding the information associated with these data. In science and engineering, the availability of adequate data is the fundamental requirement for continued progress.

We are continuing to use data, more data, better data, to assist human intuition and judgment. You can think of many examples. For instance, I have already mentioned that the Army at Fort Ord is applying a new pattern of techniques for evaluating different sorts of tactical organizations and different kinds of weapons. Formerly, this was done by carrying out tactical exercises. Some sort of a war game would be planned with referees to decide on battle damage and the place and time it occurred. The data were collected by human observers. Now the entire operation is carried out by instruments which also greatly assist in evaluating results. If you can imagine a laboratory exercise employing helicopters flying down from a hilltop, tanks coming up over the hill manned by soldiers with recoilless rifles shooting at them, and a complex automatic recording system reporting back to a central station, you can see how automatically driven pens can record all the details of battle, including an immediate designation of the winner. Not only can kills be recorded on the charts but little containers of yellow smoke can be made to appear as a signal of each kill for the combatants. This example illustrates how data availability is allowing military strategists to set up studies that show them how to take maximum advantages of technological advances in terms of deciding among available weapons, or working out the best tactics with an effectiveness beyond the dreams of even a few years ago.

The assistance for human efforts that is available from instruments and computers is today very sophisticated and beyond the comprehension of many people. For example, the Instrumentation Laboratory project to provide guidance equipment for the Apollo manned round trip to the moon deals with the most advanced technology in all the pertinent areas of science and technology. This system must be designed to make the most effective use of man and instruments in carrying out one of the most difficult and exacting tasks ever attempted by mankind. The first flights, at least on orbital missions, must be guided from takeoff to landing unmanned. Later, the same guidance system will serve the human crew as they make round trips between the surface of the earth and the surface of the moon. Guidance for Apollo is only one illustration of a complex and expensive project with objectives that are made possible only by the systematic collection of data on all essential events during the flight. These available data do far more than improve information. They provide the basis of making immediate decisions, decisions of a higher order of sophistication than has been required in all the previous history of technology. Operation of the guidance system depends upon the star sights and observations of other celestial bodies, observations that may either be optical or radar or radio or laser. The equipment used for making these observations must be stabilized in inertially maintained coordinates to permit alignment of the instrumented guidance space with the outside space in which the controlled vehicle follows a programmed path.

As a matter of practical necessity, the information associated with guidance-system operation is for the most part represented by electrical signals pulsed for compatability with digital-computer operation. Digital signals are not only useful for the purposes of computation, but are particularly well suited for the transmission of great amounts of data either locally by wires, or over indefinitely great distances by telemetry. All of the essential information within the Apollo guidance system exists in digital signal forms which actuate automatic components, work displays to inform the pilot of existing situations and to provide pulse trains for transmitting data to monitoring stations on the earth. The same signals are available to the on-board pilot and the ground. Commands in the digital signal form are accepted by the guidance equipment. Since this is so, the system may be used by the on-board pilot and the ground with equal facility except for transmission delays for the remote station. The pattern is that of available data provided by sensors in the vehicle, processing, evaluation, comparison of existing situations with planned programs, the generation of guidance commands, the application of these commands to the control system and the display of all pertinent information to the human beings concerned.

The over-all guidance arrangement for Apollo is a pioneering example of information engineering applied to a sequence of very complex problems that must be carried out accurately and continuously under particularly stringent reliability requirements. In effect, this guidance system is a model of data collection, transmission, processing, and application that includes all the general features of the information-handling subsystems that must be integrated into operations of all kinds. Powerplants, factories, laboratories and organizations of all kinds require control and guidance or working combinations of men and machines. In all situations, steps must be taken to collect, process and apply data. The Apollo guidance system illustration is a case in which the derived information has to be used immediately for continuously determining the course of events. The same information recorded and studied under more leisurely conditions is the essential input for operational analysis directed toward improvements in plans and procedures. Looked at by theoreticians and engineers, system data become the basis for technological advances in the form of improvements for existing equipment and progress in systems for the future. Success with new systems for an already opened region of technology depends very greatly on the availability of complete and accurate data on existing production designs and their performance under operational conditions. These data are generally not required for immediate use but, after periods of careful study, supply important parts of the background upon which the decisions of advancing technology are developed. In practice, the use of information in this way means documentation of all the essential data associated with the technology involved. For any particular project, documentation implies a store of systematically complete and easily retrieved concise knowledge needed to cover all essential phases from basic theory through design features, performance specifications, manufacturing information, test procedures, and operational use. As a general rule, proper documentation is expensive, accounting for a significant fraction of the total cost associated with the development of new systems. As a general rule, documentation–which is certainly the key to effective availability of data in any given field of technology–has not received its proper share of attention until very recently. For example, little or no provision for documentation was generally allowed by government contracting officers until a very few years ago and even today it is still very difficult to achieve adequate support for this essential activity. The resulting lack of available data has often been very costly in delays and money for many important projects.

During the past twenty-five years many examples of the interplay be-between development, documentation, and funds have occurred in the Laboratory. With urgency to achieve working production equipment in the hands of operational units as the central theme, technological advances have often been carried through with such rapidity that in the usual absence of adequate provisions for collecting, recording, and filing information, documentation in forms suitable for production and operational use was practically nonexistent. In some cases the time consumed in generating documentation for completed developments has been greater than the time used to complete the technological advances themselves. The other extreme occurs when funds are diverted from system-development work to such an extent that engineering tests of components and subsystems are slighted in favor of documentation. When this occurs, over-all results suffer because actual system performance falls short of the standards described by the documentation. Hard and fast rules prescribing the balance between system-development efforts and documentation are of little use; wisdom based on knowledge and experience must dictate the details of each particular situation. However, it is certain that proper documentation to insure availability of essential data is an essential feature of all projects intended to result in technological advances involving mass-produced equipment.

This statement also holds across-the-board for research and development at all levels with, of course, the provision that judgment must be applied in differentiating between records to describe frontier research and documentation associated with the technology of items to be produced in substantial quantities. Clear notebook records may be sufficient for the purposes of pioneering research while mechanized recording, computer-system storage, and automatic retrieval are demanded for production-type operations. For projects of intermediate size, documentation and access methods of any type that are workable will suffice. In all situations associated with the advancement of technology, the necessity of making all pertinent data quickly and effectively available is coming to be universally recognized. It is certain that this field of endeavor will be accorded its place of accepted importance in the future and that technology as a whole will greatly benefit from this fact.

DISCUSSION

FROM THE FLOOR: Have you received any direct support to improve your library facilities?

DR. C. S. DRAPER: We have never received any funding on any contract for a library. We do have a library. This is a fairly extensive operation where we maintain the required security restrictions on documents in possession of laboratory personnel. It's a place where information pertinent to laboratory work is available. We have not tried to build up a large reference library. The Institute itself has extensive library facilities that are available for use by the Laboratory. Each of the projects has its own responsibility for documentation and maintaining special references.

FROM THE FLOOR: How do you insure continuity in your work by project operation?

DR. C. S. DRAPER: The Laboratory is not intended to be an organization for its own sake. My aim has been to insure, so far as I am able, that my project groups do good jobs on each program. When each program is completed, I do not try to keep the responsible group together as a team. Always, if I possibly can, when another project is started I select a new leader–sometimes of necessity because laboratory people are very often attracted to industry. In other cases, changes are made because I wish to give new men chances to develop. There may be some key personnel who move across project lines; for example, the Polaris group was very successful. When the Apollo program came along I did not try to put the Apollo job into this unquestionably able group. The successful group, with unhappiness to a number of people, was not given the job; rather, a new group was built up for Apollo. By changes of this kind something is lost, but there are certainly gains to balance the losses. Substantial gains always come from giving young people, without established positions, chances to show what they can do. A good and enthusiastic group of able young scientists and engineers is pretty sure to bring fresh viewpoints to a new job. This is a most important factor in success. Once a project group has accomplished a job in a given manner, it is very difficult to get them to change viewpoints and to attack problems in new ways. The best method for introducing new approaches is to start new groups.

FROM THE FLOOR: Can you give an example of project leader development where technology was transferred to industry?

DR. C. S. DRAPER: Certainly. Along about 1950, Dr. John Hutzenlaub resigned from the Laboratory and joined the A. C. Spark Plug Company. He recruited almost the entire staff of his section in the Laboratory for A. C. This incidentially was a great help in transferring information from the Laboratory to industry because at that time our drawings were much less than ideal. Dr. Hutzenlaub and his staff were able to cut the time and cost of providing A. C. with manufacturing information. The persons who had actually carried out the design job transferred necessary information and prepared the documentation for manufacture of the inertial guidance system involved.

FROM THE FLOOR: How do you assign "Documentation" responsibilities to your project groups? How does the information get transferred?

DR. C. S. DRAPER: Each one of the project leaders has his own "library". It's hard for us to have a central library because we don't have any one building that can be called the Instrumentation Laboratory. We live in some dozen separated buildings. In the course of organizing a new project, we try to arrange space for the group concerned in a single building. In the case of Apollo the documentation is maintained in a small library devoted entirely to this project. We do not have a central library for the reason that we do not have funds, space or personnel to set it up. The Apollo group has its own library; the Polaris group has its own library; and the Sabre group has its own library. I freely admit that this is very inefficient. However, information is transferred from one group to the other by a hard core of people who have been with the Laboratory for many years and understand the processes of developing technology. Most of the people in charge of project groups have worked with me for some ten to twenty years. Their efforts and much of my own time is spent in transferring information. I try to keep my finger on events in each one of the major areas and keep essential people informed. Another means for this end are staff meetings attended by the people who carry responsibility for operating a laboratory that deals with areas of technology in the same way that scientific laboratories deal with science.

TECHNICAL INFORMATION AND DECISION-MAKING

HAROLD F. LANIER
Goodyear Aerospace Corporation
Akron, Ohio

Many of the people who use technical information are in various levels of management and program-planning. The needs of these people are quite different from those of the individual engineer and scientist. I will outline some of the problems involved and discuss some solutions.

Figure 1 lists several classes of information-users in a typical industrial situation. The classes listed progress from the individual engineer or scientist to the planning groups guiding national programs. I have tried to estimate the proportion of technical people involved in "management" functions. In our own engineering organization we find that somewhere between a half and three-fourths of all professional people are engaged at least part time in some facet of the program other than direct engineering and scientific work. Certainly it is worthwhile to discuss the technical information requirements of these groups.

It's fairly obvious that the information needs of a group starting a new kind of national program are substantially different from the needs of a group engaged in attempting to invent something or attempting to do a relatively routine improvement on an existing product.

Figure 2 depicts the progressive stages of information requirements. As you move from the top down the list you move to second order and third order characteristics of technical information; you concern yourself first with the facts themselves, and then related facts, and then with the rate of acquisition of information, and finally trends in the rate of acquisition. There are also at least two other dimensions in which level of interest changes. In the second dimension, there is a progression from isolated facts to larger fields of information. The field of interest spreads to ever broader expanses of technology with advances in level.

The next dimension is time as information needs move from past to future. Whereas the man in group one, with a problem facing him right

- **ENGINEERS OR SCIENTISTS WORKING INDIVIDUALLY**
- **SYSTEMS ENGINEERS MAKING ASSIGNMENTS**
- **LOCAL MANAGEMENT SELECTING PROJECTS**
- **R&D PROCUREMENT ACTIVITY SELECTING BOTH PROJECTS & SOURCES**
- **PLANNING GROUP GUIDING NATIONAL PROGRAM**

Figure 1. Levels of Information Requirements.

now, works with just what he can find that already exists plus what he invents himself, the group five man is working way out in the future on predictions and extrapolations.

Most collections of technical documents are not likely to contain the forward planning kind of information. Each pertinent document will contain one little point in the continuum. However, some kind of document might exist that does contain this kind of information. The chances are that any really worthwhile objective is well known and that a number of organizations will work toward it simultaneously.

The military world and the civilian world both live on simple concepts. Amorphous and complicated concepts just can't be sold. People like to live with what they can see and believe. One way to look at it is that if you can put across an idea in about two minutes then the chances are it's worthwhile and can be sold. Inertial guidance is an outstanding example of a basically simple concept that is difficult to execute and has developed into a large factor in our military structure. The chances are that the simple concept becomes widely known for what it is and, therefore, a lot of people are going to be working on it, a lot of people are going

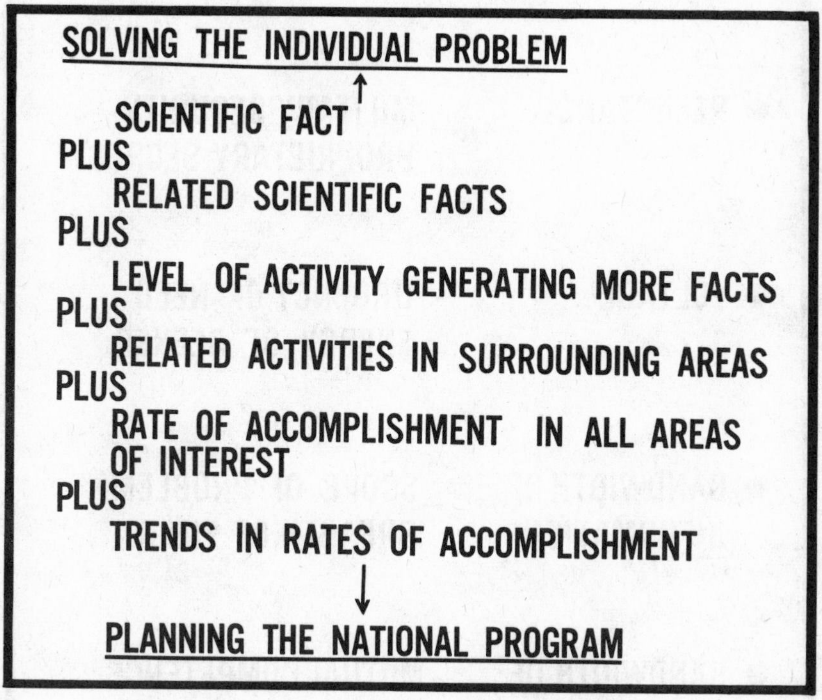

SOLVING THE INDIVIDUAL PROBLEM
↑
SCIENTIFIC FACT
PLUS
RELATED SCIENTIFIC FACTS
PLUS
LEVEL OF ACTIVITY GENERATING MORE FACTS
PLUS
RELATED ACTIVITIES IN SURROUNDING AREAS
PLUS
RATE OF ACCOMPLISHMENT IN ALL AREAS OF INTEREST
PLUS
TRENDS IN RATES OF ACCOMPLISHMENT
↓
PLANNING THE NATIONAL PROGRAM

Figure 2. Breadth of Technical Information.

to be thinking about it, a lot of people are going to understand it. In general there will be a number of competitors, a number of government activities, a number of university groups, a number of people who, more or less simultaneously, catch hold of a basic concept and who, therefore, are sources of useful information of the forward-planning type. Obviously everyone is keeping such information secret for their own benefit. What we need is a concept for getting information that is deliberately hidden, that is hard to come by, and that is a bit nebulous in nature.

Figure 3 shows a number of factors that determine the efficiency of transfer of difficult to obtain information. We'll reduce the problem to two people communicating with each other, either face to face or through one fellow extracting the documents that the other one generates, where the deliberate intent is to extract something beyond what open literature contains. First, the gain factor; here the competence of transmitter and re-

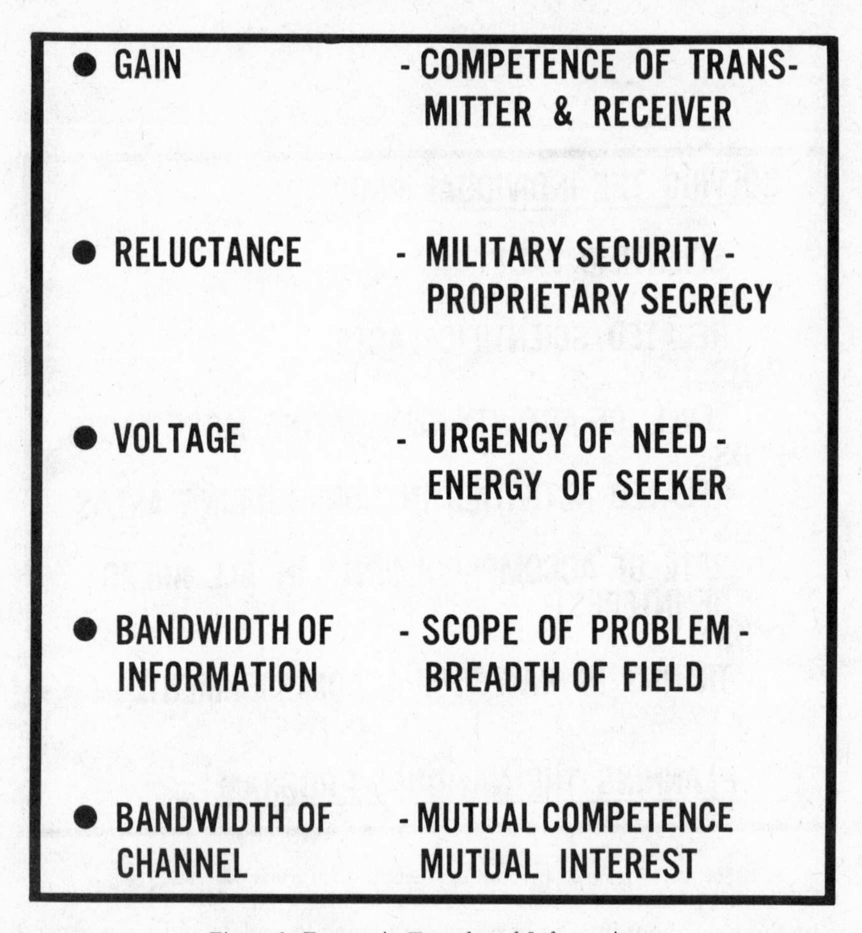

Figure 3. Factors in Transfer of Information.

ceiver is the important concern. I mean competence in the technical field of discussion, not competence as information transferers. Competence as information transferers is, in my opinion, a small factor compared with competence in the subject of discussion. This means that if a person who is truly competent in a given technical field talks to another one who is truly competent in exactly the same field his rate of information transfer will be great. In fact, such people can tell each other all there is to tell in a very short time and in a very few words. The ideas will be understood and will be fully utilized. On the other hand, people who are truly competent but not in the same field can completely lack communication.

The reluctance factor is made up of military security and proprietary secrecy. On this point I would like to say that secrecy is an individual matter. You can write as many laws as you like, yet the transfer of information is up to the individual and the individual writes his own code. Technical information transfer is not covered by a clear-cut moral code, neither is it a clear-cut legal thing. It is a question of what one feels a person should know. In the great majority of cases, intelligent people who are the possessors of technical information, who can make honorable use of the information, are qualified receptors. It is a fact that the people in our country who can really contribute in a given technical field in general are told anything they need to know in that field. They are put on advisory committees; they're made consultants; they're on interlocking boards of directors; they go to technical briefing meetings, and they're given information under the table. Almost everybody in the technical field has a tremendously strong motivation to go check his results with his compatriots who are knowledgeable and to make sure that the general rate of progress is maintained. This motivation is inherent in the majority; it is the basic drive to get the job done and done well. Another factor is bandwidth. The broader the field the more difficult to gather sufficient information. This then becomes a problem of the breadth of competence of the transmitter and receiver.

As we go through our continuum of information from the local individual problem down to planning a broad, national program, we find that information must be transmitted at progressively higher levels in the three ways previously discussed: the progression of an isoloated fact to a broad field, the progression from static information to rate of progress, and from past to future.

The next chart (Fig. 4) is based on the premise that the primary concern is the competence of the individuals concerned. As the level of concern increases, such competence must include progressively larger fields. At the second level, competence must include not only the basic technical facts themselves but how they fit together and the related facts in surrounding fields; also the nature and extent and rate of accomplishment of the activities which concern this field. In order to understand rate of accomplishment information, you must understand how information is generated, at what rates, by what kind of people, under what kind of circumstances. Certain levels of management competence must be added to the basic level of technical competence. One who wishes to find out what a rate of accomplishment is has to understand the organization employed and evaluate alternate organizations to determine whether this one's going to accomplish things faster than that one in a particular technical field. So you can see that the requirement for people who have combinations of skills is a controlling factor.

	INFORMATION GATHERING COMPETENCE
FIRST LEVEL	
SOLVE INDIVIDUAL PROBLEM	TECHNICAL SPECIALTY
SECOND LEVEL	
DECIDE APPROACH TO SOLUTION	TECHNICAL SPECIALTY PLUS KNOWLEDGE OF ACTIVITY IN THE FIELD
DEVELOP SYSTEM	SEVERAL TECHNICAL SPECIALTIES INCLUDING INTERRELATIONS
THIRD LEVEL	
CHOOSE AMONG SYSTEMS	SEVERAL TECHNICAL SPECIALTIES, INCLUDING INTERRELATIONS AND KNOWLEDGE OF ACT-IVITY IN A NUMBER OF FIELDS
PLAN A BROAD PROGRAM (FUTURE NEEDS VS FUTURE SYSTEMS)	ALL ABOVE PLUS PREDICTION OF FUTURE TECHNICAL INFORMATION AVAILABILITY

Figure 4. Competence Requirements.

Another important subject is bias. The conviction that a group of people who have done a job one way will be strongly biased in their next endeavor has been supported by research at M.I.T. The effects of past experience upon success in future R&D programs has been examined by studying cases where several companies all tried to produce a design for a given competition. The conclusion drawn was that experience that was directly applicable to the problem at hand produced a high probability of a successful solution to the problem. Organizations that had experience which they thought was applicable but was not had zero chance. They were trying to apply what they knew to a problem to which it was not quite applicable.

Where organizations in the second group deliberately broke into parts and tried alternate approaches, their probability of success approached 50 percent. The lesson is, if you move along the line of experience that is directly applicable you come up with the right answer; if your experience is not directly applicable you come up with the wrong answer. As applied to the information gathering case, it's very apparent that the selection of communicators must take bias into account. Often this requires that you bring together a group that eliminates to a fair extent the bias of competence by counterbalancing or averaging. Such a group should be aimed pretty nearly at a neutral direction so they can guide themselves along lines of logical reasoning rather than the line of bias of past experience.

All of this discussion so far has concerned itself with what you would call the straightforward case; the case where a group of people are given an assignment and that assignment is to achieve a direct objective. Unfortunately, this is not the usual case in our country. The usual case is for a variable objective to be approached by a group of people whose skills and experience may or may not be applicable. The indefinite situation is much more common than the definite.

I'll illustrate this in a couple of figures (Figs. 5 and 6). In Figure 5 we take a simple approach as to what happens. Consider a military problem which someone has observed from his past experience, or a hidden problem that comes to light when some kind of solution is observed. The next step is to determine whether R&D is required or not. Most problems can be solved with some existing apparatus or method, or just a change in the ground rules. However, most problems can also be approached on a research and development basis. That is, almost any problem could be the subject of research and almost any problem could require development. Therefore, the approach to problem solving often becomes a matter of how much money or how many people are available. The total amount of R&D effort is a question of funds and manpower rather than of the existence of problems. The decision to proceed with R&D is usually followed by a search for applicable technology. In most cases there are other similar problems which have been tackled successfully, resulting in apparatus which is more or less related to the problem at hand. From this an estimate can be made of the present state-of-the-art. Some-

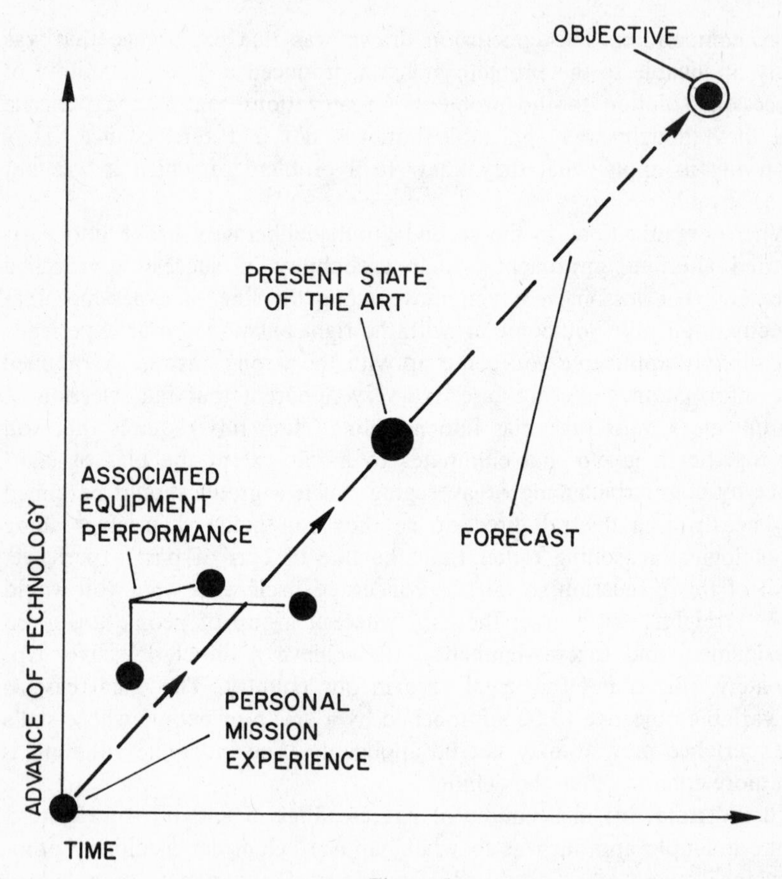

Figure 5.

times the required technology is available and can be applied in a straightforward way. As soon as the requirements are frozen the specifications are written and the developer moves straight out to the objective. By the time he gets there the thing's obsolete, of course, because new technology is available at that time. So that's not really what's done in most cases. What's really done is described in the Figure 6.

The additional factor is recognition of the large variety of things that could be done. Choices vary from a most urgent solution to the problem to the most economical. There will also be changes in the state-of-the-art which permit vertical progress.

One can, therefore, adjust the technical goals and the urgency factor. How is all this done? One goes through a succession of decision-phases where professional opinions in operational, political, economic and other fields are equated with maximum state-of-the-art estimates. One must consider not only what the state-of-the-art is today but where it will be; not what the need is today but what the need will be; not where I best accomplish this today but where I will best accomplish it with the factors that will come into play some time in the future; and what auxiliary or related programs are now being considered which, if they succeed, will produce a result which will be a significant part of this effort. You might say that all of this is largely done by speculation and intuition. There are brilliant men who just know the answers. However, as a practical matter there are a number of things that can be done in order to carry out this process on a systematic basis.

One of the obvious things is to bring together a number of people of

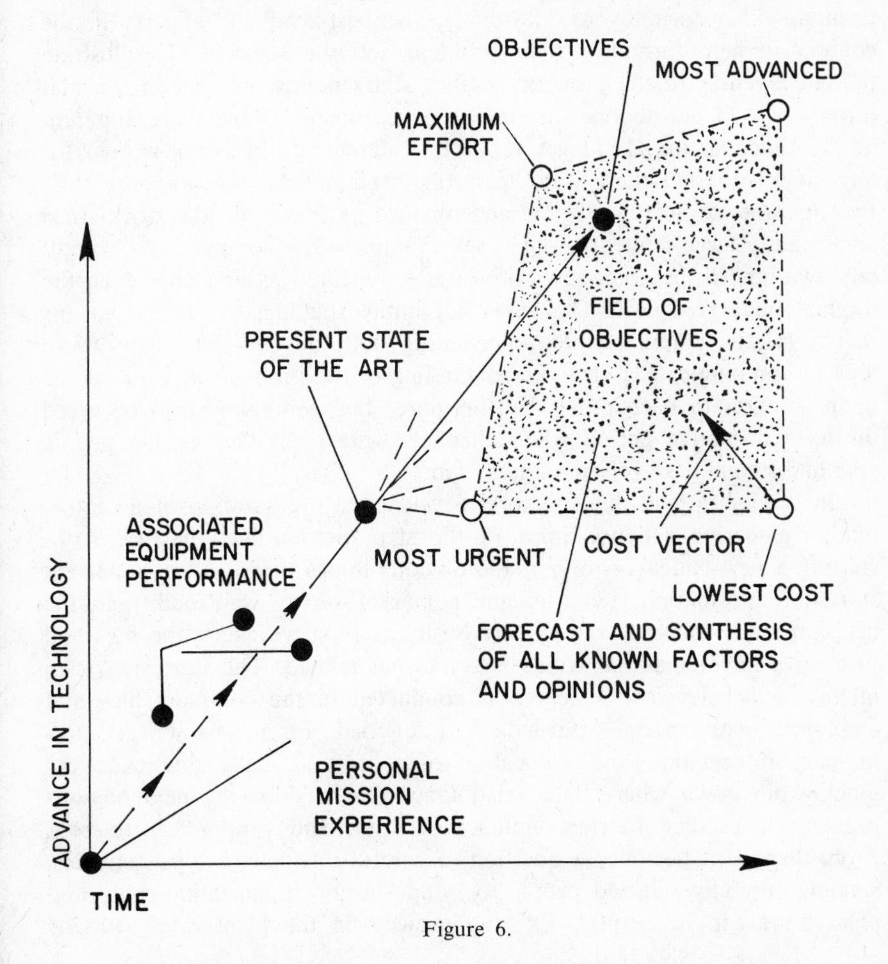

Figure 6.

complementary skills to reach a joint conclusion. This is the general process of R&D program acquisition where a combination of government studies, company R&D efforts, meetings, briefings and other interchanges consolidate the findings and opinions of a number of technically competent organizations to reach a reasonable decision. Of course, there not only must be someone in the government who wants to buy, who reaches the common conclusion, but there must be someone in industry who's willing to sell, who reaches that conclusion, and there should be more than one seller to maintain competition. It is a fact that in the process of producing this decision the actual transfer of both proprietary and military classified information becomes rather complete. The government activity which is going to start a program should, and usually does, bring together in some fashion, either formally or informally, the best available experts in the country to help formulate their problem and the solution. To illustrate the effectiveness of the process, another study points out that in the majority of R&D bid actions the one or few probable winners are apparent at the time the initial budget request is submitted. In other words, for any given program there is at least one, and most likely no more than two or three, completely logical and obvious groups to do the work. In a significantly large percentage of cases examined, the contract was eventually awarded to the company whose name appeared as first choice on the original budget request. This does not imply skulduggery. It just means that a relatively few people representing both buyers and sellers were able to communicate a clear understanding of the problem and an agreed upon solution to each other. Furthermore, this communication occurred during a formative period when channels were open and among people who had a good basis for communication.

In the light of all these factors, consider the organization of an information gathering activity. Some of the steps are outlined in Fig. 7. In starting a new endeavor, one of the obvious things to do is assess current stores of information. Let's assume a market survey was made and the decision made to break into a new business. First we check the files and turn up a lot of material which is somewhat related. The next step is to fill in the deficiencies. A search is conducted in the company files and employees with special knowledge are queried. From this we get preliminary information and a location of sources. Usually one can very quickly pin down where data exist. Once that is done the next obvious problem is secrecy barriers—military security, and proprietary interest. From then on it becomes a question of careful intelligence type activities. Sending carefully selected people to symposia and organization-sponsored plant tours can be helpful. Existing projects in the plant often provide

- **ASSESS CURRENT STORE OF INFORMATION**
- **PLAN TO FILL DEFICIENCIES**
  - **LIBRARY RESEARCH**
    PRELIMINARY INFORMATION
    LOCATION OF SOURCES
  - **INTERROGATION**
    EVALUATION OF SOURCES
    EVALUATION OF AVAILABLE INTERROGATORS
    PREPARATION
      STUDY TO IMPROVE MATCH BETWEEN SOURCE AND INTERROGATOR
      R&D TO DEVELOP TRADING INFORMATION
- **EXECUTE INFORMATION GATHERING PLAN**
- **REPORT AND DOCUMENT FOR INTERNAL USE**
- **DISSEMINATE RESULTS FOR EXTERNAL EFFECT AND TO STIMULATE FEEDBACK**

Figure 7. Information Program.

access to much data of use in a new procurement. Often data forbidden in one bidding action are freely distributed in another. However, the bulk of activity must revolve around interrogation. In this field a major concern is the evaluation of sources and the evaluation of interrogators. The question is "Who's the receiver?" "Does he understand what he has?" "Is it interpreted properly?" Consider for example the information-gathering prior to answering the following question: "Can a missile system we build provide a good answer to a postulated requirement as seen by the procuring activity?" Obviously an answer doesn't exist in anybody's literature. This becomes a difficult task. You may have to take somebody off his regular job and train him in this particular endeavor. He has to know a lot about his own company's capabilities, about the product, and about the source so he can do a reasonable job. After all, the length of time to gather this information is not indefinite. One must study to improve the match between the source and the interrogator. If they don't have a mutual competence they won't transmit a bit of information no matter how much time they spend together.

The next task is to find a reasonable basis to prove that you are technically competent so the other person will be convinced you have a need to know. This is the universal law–technical people will freely communicate only with people they believe can use the data. The expert just won't talk to people whom he doesn't think are suitable receptors.

It is necessary to have a program to generate technical information of one's own which can be used in the process of gathering new information. Then in a crucial step the interrogator must be so placed that the communication is forthcoming. This is typically a transfer in the midst of mutual problem-solving. The man with the problem must be convinced that in one way or another the transfer of the information will help solve his problem. This boils down to a firm specification on the interrogator. He must be actually capable of contributing in some way to the specific solution requiring this specific information.

The final steps are collation, analysis, and dissemination of technical data. As a consequence of information-gathering there will be a certain number of documents, written reports, trip reports, and so forth. It is usually necessary to keep a very good file of communications. The occasional nuggets of good technical information are often used over and over again and thus warrant special treatment, such as assembly into internal handbooks. The last facet concerns dissemination of results.

This is a very important point that many people miss. When you learn something worthwhile it is usually valuable to tell a lot of other people. In the first place, the fact that you learned from somebody else proves it is not yours alone. To disseminate things that you know gives you a great gain factor in that you then have improved your apparent competence level, which is the largest factor in gathering new information. Usually the smart thing to do is to avoid burying in your files anything that might be of use, provided that you did not invent it yourself. Useful technical information, carefully disseminated, will produce valuable feedback.

In conclusion, I offer the following thoughts as a means of improving our information system. In general terms, there are several steps which can be taken to improve the situation. On all levels, information gathering should be recognized as a total system involving documents and interrogation. This can profitably be under one basic management in many organizations. A branch of management science should be founded to foster professional growth in this field. The preparation for information gathering should include the steps of assessing the competence match between the source and the recipient, and this requires the development of techniques of measuring and communicating field of interest data and measuring the competence field of view and competence level. Examination of employees in this light is probably an important thing for a company to do. The cost of thorough information-gathering should be analyzed and weighed on a systematic basis and it must be recognized that costs may be high.

Many formal information systems such as libraries and retrieval systems should be reoriented towards the better handling of field of interest data and level of activity data. To reiterate, the one basic requirement for information-gathering is a suitable technical competence on the part of the gatherer. If this requirement is fully met all else will usually fall in line. As we improve information gathering we will improve the efficiency and effectiveness of that large majority of technical people who plan and guide our future.

REFERENCES

1. Industrial Liaison Symposia, "Management of Research and Development," March 5, 1964.
2. Edward B. Roberts, "How the U.S. Buys Research," *International Science and Technology* (September 1964).
3. Stanley Hiller, Jr., "Technical Competence, Basis for Change," *Army* (May 1964).

PART III

SPECIALIZED DATA/INFORMATION SOURCES AND THEIR UTILITY

DISCUSSION OF FUNCTIONS OF DATA/INFORMATION ANALYSIS CENTERS

G. S. SIMPSON, JR.
Assistant Manager
Department of Economics and Information Research
Battelle Memorial Institute
Columbus Laboratories

INTRODUCTION

This presentation is based on the following:

- An analysis of over 200 scientific data/information centers in the United States conducted in July 1961 and published in January 1962.
- A recent review of the literature pertaining to data/information centers.
- An analysis of information contributed in April and May 1964 by 33 directors of specialized data/information services supported by the U. S. Government, Industry, and Battelle.

I would like to acknowledge immediately the contributions of the respondents and those of my colleagues at Battelle. I hasten to add the contributors are not responsible for the words, method of presentation, or interpretations contained in this review.

In government, the existence and importance of specialized data/information centers has been noted not only by Senator Humphrey's subcommittee in 1961, but also by the Panel on Science Information of the President's Science Advisory Committee (PSAC) in January 1963. Over 70 persons either within government or outside have published one or more papers on "information centers" since 1961.

A quotable quote on data/information centers was made by Dr. Alvin Weinberg, Director, ORNL, and reported by *International Science and Technology Magazine in* April 1963 to wit:

> I believe that in the proliferation and strengthening of the spe-

> cialized information centers we are witnessing the beginning of a kind of social reorganization of science, a social reorganization brought about by the ever-growing difficulty of communication. . . .

With this observation in mind, it is timely, I think to devote a few minutes to consideration of the functions of specialized data/information centers. Accepting Dr. Weinberg's comment on the "ever-growing difficulty of communication," I shall define the type of specialized data/information centers I shall be discussing. I volunteered a definition for information centers in the analysis I did in 1961—and from that experience I learned that a number of people do not take kindly to definitions. Be that as it may, I hope you will accept the definition I use today not so much as *the* definition but rather in the light of an attempt at more effective communication.

DEFINITION

The specialized data/information centers (whose functions we will examine) will be referred to subsequently and variously as centers, information centers, or as Information Analysis Centers. An important initial clue to understanding the type of specialized information activity we are to examine lies in the word analysis. In some Centers the word evaluation is used instead of analysis.

Borrowing freely from the PSAC report titled "Science, Government, and Information," from some knowledge of the efforts of the Director* of Technical Information, of the DDR&E, to prepare a DOD instruction on centers for analysis of scientific and technical information, and from our experiences at Battelle, today's definition for a Data/Information analysis center is:

> One or more scientists, engineers, or information specialists, committed to providing to a specialized audience the technically intellectual service of evaluating, integrating, condensing and analyzing available information or data in a specific area of science or technology, or pertaining to a specified mission. The center provides answers to technical questions and provides to its specialized audience *authoritative* and *timely*, data arrays, analyses, monographs, or state of the art reports. Frequently an information analysis center is an adjunct of a technical organization competent in the topical areas encompassed by the scope of the center. Other information services frequently are provided including bibliographies, accession lists, and handbooks.

---

*Walter M. Carlson

A BRIEF HISTORY

Thirteen information analysis centers started in the United States in the nineteenth century. None were commercial ventures; all but one were supported by the United States or state governments. The remaining one was supported by a professional society.

With the turn of the century, new centers developed at an average rate of slightly in excess of one per year up to 1940. From 1940 to the present [May 1964] *at least* 153 additional information centers have started business. This rate of development averaged nearly seven per year since 1940. However, the greatest rise in new information centers occurred after World War II, or in 1946. Only one of the 1946 class was strictly defense oriented, namely the Johns Hopkins Applied Physics Laboratory, Chemical Propulsion Information Agency, although two others were supported by the U.S. Government.

In 1957 and 1958, the rate of growth jumped to over 15 each year because of the International Geophysical Year for which some eleven "Data" centers were established.

Most of the information centers started in 1957 were U.S. Government-supported. In 1958, however, 30 percent of the new centers were supported by nonprofit and industrial organizations.

During the period 1959 through 1963, new information analysis centers continued to develop at a rate of 5 to 7 per year. Based on our research at Battelle, we know that at least three of these new centers are operated completely by and for private industry. And, according to the June 18, 1963 Status Report on Scientific and Technical Information in the Federal Government, by the Federal Council for Science and Technology:

> There has been continued growth in the number and use of specialized information centers both within the government's own laboratories and also through support by some government agencies of information centers in subject areas of particular interest. . . . The Department of Defense leads other agencies in the number of specialized information centers receiving support. . . . The National Institutes of Health is Planning for a program of specialized information evaluation centers, three of which may be funded in FY 1963. Critical reviews, general-purpose summary monographs, and similar selective digests would be produced by each evaluation center. Similarly, the Atomic Energy Commission has already established more than a dozen such centers at its national laboratories, including two within recent months, one for radiation shielding and one for nuclear safety. Additional information centers are

being planned by other agencies to cover a wide variety of scientific and technical areas in depth.

Because of such barriers as ineffective communication, proprietary interests, and security, the precise number of U.S. information analysis centers—as we are defining them today—is not known. Estimates published regarding the number of U.S. information centers vary from a low of at least 250 (mine) to a high of 3,000, while the National Referral Center has identified considerably more information services. I am sure this wide difference is due to a difference in definition, and that if one keeps strictly to information analysis centers as defined here, we might locate up to 400 IAC's in the United States.

SIZE

The smallest-sized centers I have been able to locate (there are several of them) are composed of one scientist working part time. The largest I know about is a complex of over 250 research scientists and engineers who do information analysis on a part time basis and who are supported by a full time staff of some 80 persons.

A synthesized "average-sized" center can be thought of as having 4 full time professionals assisted by 5 part time scientists, engineers, or information specialists, and 6 full time support personnel.

PERSONNEL

Table 1 shows the number and types of personnel working in 221 information analysis centers as of 1961.

TABLE 1

NUMBER OF PERSONNEL BY TYPES IN 221 U. S. SCIENTIFIC INFORMATION CENTERS ANALYZED IN 1961[5]

Types of Personnel	Full Time	Part Time
Information specialists	465	275
Scientists/engineers	1,404	681
Computer personnel	315	66
Semiprofessional	1,066	238
Nonprofessional	1,163	231
Total	4,413	1,491

The applicability of these numbers to the year 1964 is such as to suggest an increase in the ratio of part-time personnel to full-time personnel, and an over-all increase in both. Considering the centers that are known to have come into being since 1961, most of them are utilizing a greater percentage of part-time scientists and engineers than were many of the centers analyzed in Table 1.

RANGE OF ANNUAL COSTS OF INFORMATION ANALYSIS CENTERS

The variation in costs of known information analysis centers ranges from a low in the $10,000 per year class to several approaching the million-dollar class. From among the small number of centers for which there is enough information currently available to be able to obtain a fix on annual costs, the biggest percentage cost in the range of $200,000 per year. I know of only 6 costing over $3–4 million per year but I speculate there may be a few more in this class.

Admittedly these comments on costs are not very precise, I mention them nevertheless because they indicate not only the lack of information on the question of costs of information centers but also that the variation is very wide. Generally those centers supported by industry, universities, and nonprofit institutions are not so large as those of the government.

FUNCTIONS

Functions of organizational entities can be examined from several viewpoints. In the case of Information Analysis Centers, I have chosen, logically I hope, two viewpoints–one from (1) the expressed needs of potential users of three proposed centers and (2) functions of operating services as viewed by some 33 center directors.

For information on the first viewpoint I have used three reports and will list their findings. For the second viewpoint–I shall use the essence of the letters and telephone calls received from the respondents included the references.

FUNCTIONS OF ANTICIPATED DATA/INFORMATION ANALYSIS CENTERS

On at least three recent occasions, to justify and properly design proposed government-supported information centers, user audiences and existing information sources have been surveyed to determine:

- If there were such a center, would it be useful?
- Whether there are existing information sources which significantly duplicate the services of the proposed center?
- What types of products and services the user audience needed?

The number of "users" and existing information sources contacted ranged from a low 23 users and 25 information sources to a high of over 200 users and 25 information sources. In the low group, of 23 users contacted, 14 responded; in the higher group approximately 200 responded.

Integrating the findings of each survey, a summary statement can be made as follows:

- The proposed centers would be useful.
- The proposed centers will duplicate to an extent some present information services but will provide sufficiently unique and valuable services to warrant their existence.
- The users' needs are similar in total but vary in detail as shown in Table 2.

TABLE 2

USERS NEEDS AS REVEALED BY SURVEY OR ESTIMATED BY INTERPRETATION OF ALLOCATION OF EFFORT FOR THREE PROPOSED CENTERS

Service Needed	Source A Reported	Source B Estimated	Source C Reported
State-of-the-arts reports	1	X (1)	1
Quick response to inquiries	2	X (2)	3
Special memo reports	7	X (3)	7
Bibliographies	6	X (4)	5
Accession lists	5	—	8
Abstracts	—	—	2
Serve visitors	4	—	6
Data sheets, routine	8	X	9
Data sheets, special request	3	X } (1)	4
Compendia	9	X	10

I would like to emphasize that this comparison is present only to indicate the types of functions that three different user audiences expect of a potential information center intended to serve their three technical areas. Based on previous analyses, these "user needs" are typical. It is appropriate to point out, too, that such functions as preparation of bibliographies, accession lists, and abstracts also are provided by many other information services such as libraries, special libraries, and abstract journal publishers. Although the users are aware of the other information services, they still believe they need a service tailored specifically to their specialized area. If such a service can be provided and if it will save them "information work," obviously they would be in favor of such a service.

How these users of potential centers might react if they were to be billed for the services rendered is another question–one that brings forth different answers. One answer frequently given is that if the government didn't pay for the center, it wouldn't exist. This could be–however, in the 1961 analysis of information centers I mentioned earlier, of over 200 centers, 97 were directly supported by the U.S. Government, and 97 were funded by private industry, professional societies, and research institutions.

FUNCTIONS OF EXISTING DATA/INFORMATION ANALYSIS CENTERS

At Battelle there are a dozen information analysis centers. Of these, five are supported by the Department of Defense, AEC and NASA, and seven are supported either by a single sponsor, a group of sponsors, or by Battelle itself. To decrease the probability that I might provide you a restrictive, narrow, or parochial description of center functions, 32 information centers, not at or operated by Battelle were contacted by letter or telephone. Some of these centers are strictly private, but most of them are supported by the U.S. Government either in house, or on contract.

The over-all number contacted was 44, including those contacted at Battelle. Of these six are privately funded, the balance of 38 are government funded.

Of the 6 nongovernment centers contacted, all responded and 33 government supported centers responded. Of all that responded, 8 did not provide usable information–for valid reasons–hence our sample is composed of 31 centers.

At this point I would like to express again my thanks to those who did respond. A number of the center managers or directors sent me very detailed letters which discussed not only the functions they perform, but also indicated their views of their future requirements. Some included brochures, annual reports, and fliers. Two respondents indicated their services are not yet classed as information centers; one responded with a comprehensive letter which included his observation that the questions I raised are being asked of him continuously; another respondent advised his center is, strictly speaking, yet to be; and one didn't care to provide any information because he needed certain clarifications I couldn't supply.

Altogether the responses are so comprehensive that it is possible only to transfer but a portion of their content.

To increase the probability that the centers would report all significant functions, the center directors contacted were requested by letter simply to provide an estimate of the percent of their effort devoted to the several functions their centers perform. A structured questionnaire was not used. As a result, the directors reported the functions of their centers in their words. A compilation of the functions reported, and the rough estimates of the percent of effort applied to each function is contained in Table 3. All of the functions presented were mentioned one or more times by the respondents. I had to do some interpreting, of course, for example: I included the function of preparation of data sheets as part of data analysis and in some cases, where the Director lumped the functions of acquisition, storage, and retrieval together, I placed part of the effort in acquisition, since by far most of the Directors reported acquisition separately.

At first I would have imagined that "technical evaluation" would be considered synonymous with state of the art and data analysis. However, three of the four directors who listed technical evaluation as a function also listed state of the art analysis as a function. For this reason technical evaluations are listed as another function.

Another interesting vagary in reporting is that but six directors identify administration or management as a function of their center, and vote the range–from 2 to 25 percent.

Interpretation of Compilation

The compilation (Table 3) is arranged so that the most frequently reported functions are at the top. Those functions mentioned less frequently follow, for example, "answering questions," whether received by phone, letter or visits was mentioned as a function 31 times, "acquisition" was mentioned 30 times. These two functions are at the top followed by state-of-the-art and data analysis, storage and retrieval and so on. Of course, this arrangement ignores weighting the percent of effort. To include the percent of effort, as well as the range in the percentages reported, I simply arranged, for each of the top eight functions, the percentages from the smallest to the largest, marked off the smallest fourth and largest fourth and selected in the middle half the median percentage.

FUNCTIONS	1	2	3	4	5	6	7	8	9	10	11	12	13	14	15	16	17	18	19	20	21	22	23	24	25	26	27	28	29	30	31	32	33	34	35	36	37	38	39	NUMBER OF RESPONSES PER FUNCTION
Answer questions, phone, letter, visits	NO ESTIMATE	NOT A CENTER	20*	13	15	30	4	—	x	NO ESTIMATE	20	4	35	10	—	x‡	4	25	2	25	NO ESTIMATE	NO ESTIMATE	5	5	6	15	20	10	6	30	10	30	NOT A CENTER	20	x‡	20	5	15	30	31
Acquisition			—	5	5	15	—	12	x }60		8	5	10	8	10	x	12	10	5	30			10	5	12	10	15	10	10	20	x	10		—	x	20	10	25	25	30
State-of-the-art, and Data analysis			—	7	35	15	22	20	—		—	—	—	25	10	x	—	—	20	15			5	35	23	—	—	65	50	15	25	16		—	x	30	60	50	—	22
Store, retrieve			—	50	15	—	—	—	x		—	60	40	—	65	x	34	50	5	—			50	30	21	60	45	—	15	—	x 60	28		—	x	—	10	—	25	21
Publish and external dissemination			80	—	15	—	—	—	x		—	—	—	7	5	x	—	5	—	—			—	—	15	—	5	—	—	20	—	12		—	x	20	—	10	—	14
Literature searches and bibliographies			—	—	—	—	—	1	—		—	—	—	5	—	WHEN ACTIVATED EXPECTS TO →	—	—	—	30			30	—	—	10	15	—	—	15	5	—		—	x	—	10	—	20	11
Administration or management			—	25	10	—	—	—	10		—	—	—	—	—		—	10	—	—			—	—	15	—	—	—	—	—	—	2		—	—	—	—	—	—	6
Advisory or Consolation service			—	—	—	—	15	—	—		—	—	5	—	—		50	—	—	—			—	25	6	—	—	—	—	—	—	—		—	—	—	—	—	—	5
Tech evaluation and news letters			—	—	—	—	—	—	—		—	—	—	30	—		—	—	47	—			—	—	—	5	—	15	—	—	—	—		—	x	—	—	—	—	5
Accession lists			—	—	5	—	—	—	—		—	—	—	5	—		—	—	1	—			—	—	2	—	—	—	—	—	—	2		—	—	—	—	—	—	5
Lab research			—	—	—	—	60	—	—		40	—	—	—	—		—	—	20	—			—	—	—	—	—	—	—	—	—	—		—	—	—	—	—	—	3
Prepare handbooks			—	—	—	—	—	65	—		25	—	—	—	—		—	—	—	—			—	—	—	—	—	—	—	—	—	—		10	—	—	—	—	—	3
Improving present operation			—	—	—	—	—	—	—		—	—	10	—	5		—	—	—	—			—	—	—	—	—	—	—	—	—	—		—	—	—	—	—	—	2
Conduct seminars			—	—	—	—	—	—	—		—	—	—	—	—		—	—	—	—			—	—	—	—	—	—	19	—	—	—		70	—	—	—	—	—	2
Provide briefings and lectures			—	—	—	35	—	—	—		—	—	—	—	—		—	—	—	—			—	—	—	—	—	—	—	—	—	—		—	—	—	—	—	—	1
Act as secretariat			—	—	—	—	—	—	30		—	—	—	—	—		—	—	—	—			—	—	—	—	—	—	—	—	—	—		—	—	—	—	—	—	1
Make technical films			—	—	—	—	—	—	—		—	—	—	10	—		—	—	—	—			—	—	—	—	—	—	—	—	—	—		—	—	—	—	—	—	1
Special calculations			—	—	—	—	—	—	—		7	—	—	—	—		—	—	—	—			—	—	—	—	—	—	—	—	—	—		—	—	—	—	—	—	1
Conduct exhibits			—	—	—	5	—	—	—		—	—	—	—	—		—	—	—	—			—	—	—	—	—	—	—	—	—	—		—	—	—	—	—	—	1

*Most percentages reported as rough estimates, hence not all total 100 percent.
†The position of the respondents in source list is intentionally scrambled and not related to respondent number shown here.
‡x indicates that respondent named the function but did not provide estimate of percent of effort.

TABLE 3 COMPILATION OF RESPONDENTS ESTIMATES

Using this method, and arraying the results descending from largest median percent the pattern shown in Fig. 1 is developed.

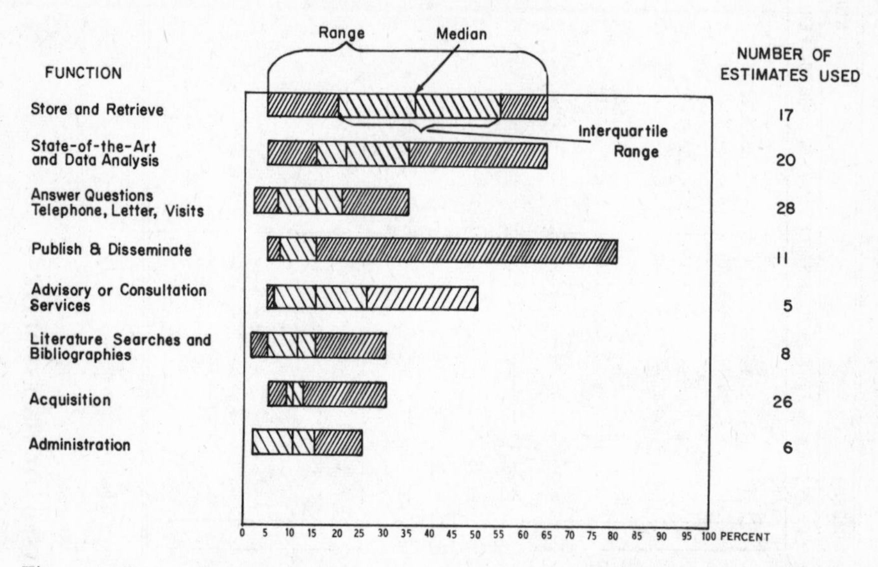

Figure 1. Range, Interquartile Range, and Medians of Efforts Estimated for Eight Functions of Data/Information Centers

Recognizing the significance of the sample size [31 of 400 (?)], the wide variation in the range of the estimates, and that the responses were intentionally "free" as contrasted with structured, I do not intend to draw rigid conclusions from the median percentages indicated. However, the pattern revealed is reasonable. For example, if we normalize the median percentages of the eight most frequently reported functions (136) to a base of 100, we find that median percentages for eight functions of "a hypothetical data/information analysis center," are

Item	*Percent*
Acquisition	8
Storage and retrieval	27
State of-the-Art and Data Analyses	16
Answer questions	11
Publish and disseminate	11
Provide consultation services	11
Conduct literature searches and prepare bibliographies	9
Administration	7
Total	100

In terms of input output, these hypothetical proportions suggest that a center spends 35 cents of each dollar on input, 58 cents on output, and 7 cents managing the center.

Discipline- or Mission-Oriented

The directors were asked whether they considered their center to be discipline-oriented, mission-oriented, or both.

Their responses were, mission-oriented 15, discipline-oriented 12, both 9; of the 6 private centers contacted, 4 consider their centers to be mission-oriented.

Expansion

The directors also were asked whether there was a need for expansion of their particular center. A count of their responses shows 26 indicate a need for expansion, 6 do not see a need for expansion, 2 refused to comment, one because he thought it would be presumptuous, and 3 were not sure.

I think most of us would expect all the directors to say their centers should be expanded. However, those directors who indicate a need for expansion carefully explained why, and under what conditions. To a man, the directors are sensitive to, I suspect, a retort of "Empire building." Among the reasons given why the centers should be expanded are (1) more users, (2) greater scope, and (3) greater dissemination and increasing publication costs.

CONCLUDING OBSERVATIONS

- The increasing number of data/information analysis centers represents not only a partial solution to the quantitative aspects of the information problem but also an increasing acceptance that to be able to stay current requires the formal establishment of groups of professionals committed, at least in part, to that assignment.
- Data/information analysis centers provide scientific and technical services to specialized audiences, including management.
- The functions of data/information analysis centers vary in detail but are, in total, similar.
- Data/information analysis centers, while seemingly costly, are not so expensive as the "estimated" cost of *not knowing*. Information analysis centers are, in a sense, intelligence centers, and must maintain a continuing aggressive acquisition program as well as a keen awareness of the user's needs.

- A most important development to look for is increasing cross-talk among data/information analysis centers.
- The growth of data/information analysis centers does not suggest that such information services as libraries, abstracting services, and document depots are decreasing in importance. Rather, centers represent specialized areas of science and technology wherein the need to be authoritatively current justifies the cost.
- There is still a reluctance on the part of scientists and engineers to become involved in data/information analysis center activities.

REFERENCES

1. John Maranchik, Jr., Arthur L. Holt, et al., "Final Report on the Design of a System for Collecting, Evaluating, and Disseminating Machinability Data for Aerospace Materials," Report Nr ASD-TDR-63-572, July 1963, prepared under Contract AF 33(657)-8796 by Metcut Research Associates, for AFSC, USAF.

2. E. M. Simons, A. W. Lemmon, Jr., et al., "An Information Center Scoping Study," September 30, 1963, carried out by BMI for Division of Technical Information, USAEC.

3. W. E. Chapin, G. L. McCann, and W. H. Veazie, Jr., "A Study of Requirements for the Establishment and Operation of a Transducer Information Center," Report Nr ASD-TDR-64, April 15, 1964, prepared by BMI under contract AF 33(657)-11083 for AFSC, USAF.

4. I. J. Panning, B. A. Frautschi, W. H. Veazie, Jr., et al., "Survey and Analysis of Specialized Science Information Service in the United States," September, 1962, prepared by BMI under Contract to NSF, Report Nr NP-12318, AEC.

5. G. S. Simpson, Jr., "Scientific Information Centers in the United States," *American Documentation,* Vol. 13, No. 1 (January 1962).

6. Drafts Number 1 and 2 (unpublished, unofficial), dated 31 December 1963 and 23 March 1964, Department of Defense Instruction. Subject: Centers for Analysis of Scientific and Technical Information being prepared by DDR&E, OSD.

7. T. P. Kridler and G. S. Simpson, Jr., "Scientific Information Centers in the U.S.A. and U.S.S.R.," *International Science and Technology* (June 1964).

8. Letters, telephone calls, and/or memo's received during the period April 1 thru May 7, 1964 from:

Name	Address
David M. Goodman Director Project SETE	New York University College of Engineering 401 West 205th Street New York 34, New York
W. C. Jacobs Director National Oceanographic Data Center	Washington, D.C. 20390
S. Vigo, Acting Chief Materials Testing Laboratory Nondestructive Testing Information Retrieval System	U. S. Army Materiels Research Agency Watertown, Mass. 02172
Patrick J. Martin Director Chemical Propulsion Information Agency	Applied Physics Laboratory The Johns Hopkins University 8621 Georgia Avenue Silver Spring, Md.
M. A. Long Assistant Chief, Special Projects Group Battelle-DEFENDER	Battelle Memorial Institute Columbus Laboratories 505 King Avenue Columbus, Ohio 43201
John D. DeCoursey Captain MSC, USN Officer in Charge Military Entomology Information Service	Department of Defense Armed Forces Pest Control Board Forest Glen Section, WRAMC Washington, D.C. 20012
Albert R. Dawe Chief Scientist Hibernation Information Exchange	Department of the Navy Office of Naval Research Branch Office 230 N. Michigan Avenue, Chicago, Ill. 60601
John Murdock Project Director, Remote Area Conflict Information Center	Battelle Memorial Institute Columbus Laboratories 505 King Avenue Columbus, Ohio 43201
Richard H. Moore, Colonel (Retd) Counterinsurgency Information Center (CICENTER) Special Operations Research Office	American University 5010 Wisconsin Avenue, N.W. Washington 16, D.C.

William Wolfe Group Supervisor IRIA	The University of Michigan Post Office Box 618 Ann Arbor, Mich. 48107
Roger Runck, Director Defense Metals Information Center	Battelle Memorial Institute Columbus Laboratories 505 King Avenue Columbus, Ohio 43201
Albert J. Belfour, President Mechanical Properties Data Center	Belfour Engineering Company Suttons Bay, Mich.
Allen P. Blade Coordinator Engineering Design Handbook Series	U. S. Army Research Office Box CM Duke Station Durham, N. C.
Peter King, Associate Director of Research for Materials	U. S. Naval Research Laboratory Washington, D.C. 20390
R. A. Yereance, Projector Director Electronic Components Reliability Center	Battelle Memorial Institute Columbus Laboratories 505 King Avenue Columbus, Ohio 43201
John W. Teare, Director Champion Information Center	Champion Papers-Knightsbridge Hamilton, Ohio
Paul G. Ronco, Director Human Engineering Information and Analysis Service	Tufts University Medford, Mass. 02155
Daniel R. Stull Thermal Research Laboratory 574 Building	The Dow Chemical Company Midland, Mich.
Charles Brophy, Librarian BMI Library	Battelle Memorial Institute Columbus Laboratories 505 King Avenue Columbus, Ohio 43201
Harry E. Pebly, Jr. Chief, PLASTEC	Picatinny Arsenal Dover, New Jersey 07801
Eugene Wyler, Project Director Radiation Effects Information Center	Battelle Memorial Institute Columbus Laboratories 505 King Avenue Columbus, Ohio 43201

H. W. Serig, Secretary
Advisory Group on Electron Devices
346 Broadway, 8th Floor
New York, N. Y. 10013

Milton E. Stevens
Lt. Colonel, CE
Director, Coastal Engineering Research Center
Corps of Engineers, U. S. Army
5201 Little Falls Road N.W.
Washington, D.C. 20016

H. Thayne Johnson, Supervisor
Electronic Properties Information Center
Hughes Aircraft Company
Culver City, Calif.

B. Frautschi
Information Specialist
Information Research Center
Battelle Memorial Institute
Columbus Laboratories
505 King Avenue
Columbus, Ohio 43201

S. W. Bradstreet,
Technical Manager
Ceramic and Graphite Information Center
AF Materiels Laboratory
W-PAFB, Ohio

F. R. Morral, Project Director
Cobalt Information Center
Battelle Memorial Institute
Columbus Laboratories
505 King Avenue
Columbus, Ohio 43201

Warren W. Chan
Manager—DASA Data Center
c/o TEMPO, The General Electric Company
735 State Street
Santa Barbara, Calif. 93102

T. W. Caless
Research Associate
Principal Investigator
VESIAC
University of Michigan
Post Office Box 618
Ann Arbor, Mich. 48107

L. B. Allen
IBM, General Products Division
Development Laboratory
Endicott, N. Y. 13764

Paul S. Balas
Director
Power Information Center of the Interagency Advanced Power Group
Moore School Building
200 South 33rd Street
Philadelphia, Pa. 19104

Bruce McCreary Information Specialist	Reynolds Metals Company Metallurgical Research Laboratories Fourth and Canal Streets Richmond 19, Va.
Y. S. Touloukian Director Thermophysical Properties Research Center	Purdue University Research Park 2595 Yeager Road West Lafayette, Ind.
T. F. Connolly, Director Research Materials Information Center	Oak Ridge National Laboratory P. O. Box Y Oak Ridge, Tenn.
Rodney P. Elliott Senior Metallurgist Constitution of Binary Alloys Review	IIT Research Institute 10 W. 35th Street Chicago 16, Ill.
S. K. Penny, Director Shielding Information Center	Oak Ridge National Laboratory P. O. Box Y Oak Ridge, Tenn.
W. W. Mutch Head, R&D Centralizing Activity for Shock, Vibration and Associated Environments	U. S. Naval Research Laboratory Washington, D.C. 20390
Philip Baker, Director Isotopes Information Center	Oak Ridge National Laboratory P. O. Box Y Oak Ridge, Tenn.
Bruce Ewbank Nuclear Data Project	Oak Ridge National Laboratory P. O. Box Y Oak Ridge, Tenn.
Wm. B. Cottrell, Director Nuclear Safety Information Center	Oak Ridge National Laboratory P. O. Box Y Oak Ridge, Tenn.

PATENTS: A VALUABLE INFORMATION SOURCE FOR RESEARCH

PAUL W. HOWERTON
The American University

INTRODUCTION

Patents constitute the most compact and easily identifiable literature resource available in which cause and effect are shown with a minimum verbiage. They also constitute a rarely used source of technical information unless the novelty of an apparently new product or process is to be tested–they are probably the least understood and yet most criticized technical information source we have.

What Exactly Is a Patent?

A patent is a grant by a government to an inventor (or his heirs or assigns) of certain exclusive rights to his invention usually for a fixed period of time. All of the principal countries of the world grant patents including the USSR. Since a patent is, in effect, a monopoly, it is interesting that the communist countries would even allow such a capitalistic tool in their administrative processes. In the examples cited in this paper will be found evidence of the relative importance of patent rights on an international level.

Strictly speaking and in the language of the U.S. statute, the right which is granted by the U. S. Government is "to exclude others from making, using or selling" the invention. The inventor is *not* granted the the right to make, use or sell, but rather to exclude others from doing so. In some countries however the patent must be used within three years or the rights may be voided or compulsory licensing may be required.

What May Be Patented?

By and large the definition of patentability is universal with only technical variation from country to country. The discovery of a "new and useful" process, machine, manufactured item or composition of matter or "new and useful" improvements on existing processes, machines, or compositions of matter constitute invention. A process or method of accomplishing a useful purpose not previously known may be patented. The term "machine" is subject to little, if any, misinterpretation. "Composition of matter" usually has to do with chemical discoveries and may include mixtures as well as new chemicals. One may easily see that these definitions comprehend almost anything made by man and the methods used.

Note that I have used the word "useful" several times. The courts have held that an invention must serve some useful purpose and must work as alleged. The classic example of claimed invention which has plagued the Patent Offices of the world is the so-called "perpetual-motion machine".

If what is believed to be a true invention has been described in a printed publication anywhere in the world, or has been in public use or sale more than one year before an application for patent is made, no patent may be granted under U.S. law. When the invention was made or if the inventor himself describes the invention in print or sells it, has no bearing on the patentability of the discovery. If differences are obvious between what is claimed to be an invention and something which has previously been patented or disclosed, no patent may be granted.

In writing a patent application, the inventor must describe his invention in sufficient detail to permit anyone who, in patent language, is "skilled in the art" to make and use the invention. A description of how this invention differs from related subjects must be provided. The object of the invention must be detailed. Because of these requirements, technical information or data of both a positive and negative nature may be given, and the patent will frequently be the *sole source* of information of a negative nature. For example, in the case of pesticide patents, a family of chemical compounds may have been synthesized and tested. Only one member of the family has real utility, but the comparative data can throw light on all members of the family concerning the relationship of chemical composition to biological activity.

A patent granted in the United States has no effect outside this country. Inventors must apply for foreign patents if they wish to protect their inventions from exploitation in foreign countries. The International Convention for the Protection of Industrial Property to which over forty countries (but not the United States) are signatory guarantees that each country extends the rights and privileges of patents to the citizens of other countries that are allowed its own people. The initial patent application made in one of the signatory countries establishes the priority data of the invention. Most countries require that application must be filed in their Patent Offices within one year of this priority date. This date is referred to as the "Convention Date".

Our laws do not discriminate against foreign applicants for American patents. In fact in 1963 one-sixth of all U.S. patents covering chemical or chemically related inventions were granted to foreign patentees. There was even one patent granted to a Russian firm. Germany leads the countries from which patent applications are received by the U.S. Patent Office. Several of the East German chemical companies have received U.S. patents. The other countries, in order of significant numbers of chemical patents issued to their citizens, are Great Britain, France, Japan, Switzerland and Italy. The over-all average for the 14 years of 1950-1963, inclusive, was: 11.2 percent of all chemical patents issued in United States went to foreign applicants. Surveillance of these patents provides useful commercial intelligence to the internationally minded American chemical industry.

FOREIGN PATENT SYSTEMS*

Close regard of foreign patents will provide advance information on discoveries of American industry. For example, a French patent granted on November 25, 1963 to E. I. du Pont de Nemours indicates that the company made application in France exactly to the day one year after the American application was filed. The U.S. Patent had not yet issued, and furthermore if one enquired at the U.S. Patent Office about the status of the application which is cited by number on the French patent, the U.S. Patent Office would have had no comment to make. The French Patent Office makes no search for novelty, but only to ensure that the application is legal according to form. Thus, French patents appear in 8–9 months after filing except under special circumstances when they are held up by request for delay. In any case they issue in one year from application. Approximately half of all French patent applications originate outside of France with the United States as the leader of the list of the foreign applicants.

Belgian patent applications are available for public inspection three months after the grant of the patent which is made within one month of

* The most complete source of information on foreign patents and patent systems is Derwent Information Service, Rochdale House, Theobald's Road, London W.C. 1, United Kingdom. Much of the information in my discussion of foreign patents was taken from Derwent publications.

application. If a delay is requested, the patents are publicly displayed six months after the filing date. Thus, Belgian patents are a very real source of advance information on inventions. The catch is that the only place where the patent may be examined is at the Belgian Patent Office. The "Recueil des Brevets d'Invention" will list the grant and the principal claim about 15 months after the filing date, but applications are listed about 2 months after the filing date in "Revue Gevers des Brevets et Repertoire des Brevets Belges Recents." Because no examination for novelty is made by the Belgian Patent Office, comparison of the language of the Belgian patent with the U.S. Patent, when granted, will show what modifications, if any, were required by the American examiner.

In the section of the German "Patentblatt" titled "Patentanmeldungen" are listed the new patents which are open to public inspection. These new patents are called "Auslegeschriften" and are printed on green paper to distinguish them from the finally approved "Patentschriften" which issue after a three-month delay for the entering of oppositions to the grant of the patent. New compositions of matter are not patentable as such in Germany, but only the method of production may be claimed. *These process patents may have no equivalent in the United States.*

In an article in the May 10, 1964 issue of the *New York Times,* the sharp increase in Japanese patents is discussed. In 1961, 175,022 applications were filed in Japan; in 1962, 214,253; and in 1963 the estimate is that 265,000 applications were filed of which 90 percent were from Japanese sources. Of these totals, patents were granted in about 55 percent of the cases. The Japanese have been criticized as mere copiers of foreign inventions, but now they are finding that their discoveries are being copied abroad. Koichi Suzuki, a director of the Japan Export Trade Promotion Agency, said that one of the main purposes of his agency was "to destroy the old image of cheap Japanese goods. . . ." Hitachi, Japan's largest industrial firm, has over 1,000 people in its technical research institute, while Toyo Rayon has a research staff over 2,800. Japanese patents constitute a very real source of technical information and data on Japanese research. It is indeed a pity that so few American research organizations have facilities for using these patents because of the language barrier.

In the United Kingdom patent applications are listed by applicant's name, the title of the invention and the country and date of original filing in *Official Journal (Patents).* The average delay from filing a complete specification and issuance of the patent is about two years. Although this delay may not provide advance information on U.S. application, it does not invalidate the usefulness of this body of literature. Applications made from outside the UK after national patents have been sought in the home country of the applicants will provide English language versions of foreign language original patents and may save the time and costs of translation since the original application must be cited in the British patent.

The Soviet Union has a patent system somewhat similar to that of Germany and in a few respects similar to ours. Although the Soviet statute provides for three types of invention–discoveries, rationalization proposals, and inventions–only the latter two are of real significance as sources of technical information. The "discoveries" are very scarce and usually are laws of nature. The "rationalization proposals" are suggestions for improvement of a process, but do not constitute real invention as we think of the term. However, as a source of technical information, they may prove valuable. Details of these plant suggestions are published irregularly as pamphlets and are available from the Technical Bookstore in Moscow or through the bookstores here which specialize in Soviet publications. The true invention may be covered by an author's certificate or a patent. In the former case the inventor is acknowledged by the Government and receives a sum of money if the invention is used by the State. A patent grants the exclusive rights to the invention to the inventor, but only about 1 percent of the inventions are covered by patents. Within four months of filing an application, the inventor must be notified of the acceptance or rejection of his invention. Publication of the disclosure and its citation in the *Byulleten' Izonbretenii Tovarnykh Znakov* (Bulletin of Inventions and Trademarks) is usually about a year after filing although the file is open to inspection in the Patent Office. Soviet author's certificates do not have detailed disclosures, but they are certainly citable against patent applications outside the Soviet Union.

A frequently heard statement by people unfamiliar with the content and timing of foreign patents to the effect that the patent literature is of little value because of the lateness of the information compared with other sources simply cannot be substantiated. Many companies both here and abroad will not allow publication of technical papers until a patent application has been acted upon and the substance of the invention made public. This means, of course, that often the first publicly available patent or application will be the first information available on the discovery.

To the international marketing people of a company, the patent provides several valuable bits of protection against mistakes in international trade. American patents can be used to prevent imports to the United States if the imported thing can be shown to infringe the claims of a U.S. patent. The Tariff Commission will see that the imports are stopped at the border. Foreign patents owned by U. S. companies can protect against the

United States Patent Office

3,086,913
Patented Apr. 23, 1963

1

3,086,913
SYSTEMIC FUNGICIDES

James M. Hamilton, 574 S. Main St., and Michael Szkolnik, R.D. 2, both of Geneva, N.Y., and Ernest Sondheimer, Geneva, N.Y. (956 Westmoreland Ave., Syracuse 10, N.Y.)

No Drawing. Continuation of application Ser. No. 615,752, Oct. 15, 1956. This application Apr. 27, 1962, Ser. No. 190,767
6 Claims. (Cl. 167—65)

This invention relates to novel compositions of matter and to a novel process and is particularly directed to novel compositions and a novel process for the controlling of plant diseases.

Cycloheximide is an antibiotic substance produced as an elaboration product of *Streptomyces griseus* according to the procedures set forth in U.S. Patents 2,574,519 and 2,612,502; by Leach et al. in J. Am. Chem. Soc. 69, 474 (1947); and by Ford et al. in J. Am. Chem. Soc. 70, 1223–1225 (1948). Cycloheximide has been found to be an effective fungicide and to be particularly useful in the control of plant diseases.

It is known that when cycloheximide is reacted with acetic anhydride, the acetate, melting point 148–149 degrees centigrade, is obtained. This compound has heretofore been thought to be biologically inactive. See Ford et al. and Leach et al. supra. Although Leach et al. report a diacetate, it was subsequently found that cycloheximide contains only one hydroxyl group and that the acetate was really the monoacetate. See Ford et al., supra, and Kornfeld et al., J. Am. Chem. Soc. 71, 150–159 (1949). Various other known derivatives of cycloheximide also have been considered to be inactive or to have little value when compared with cycloheximide.

It has now been found that certain derivatives of cycloheximide are effective for the control of plant fungal diseases, and that quite surprisingly the compounds are translocated so that new foliage growth is protected as well as the treated foliage. This is surprising because cycloheximide is not translocated. It is a surface protectant and also acts to eradicate established infections in the treated foliage.

The derivatives of cycloheximide which have been found to be effective are the carboxylic acid esters, particularly the lower alkanoic acid esters, such as the acetate, and the derivatives which are formed by reaction with the keto group of cycloheximide, such as the oxime, the semicarbazone, dehydrocycloheximide, anhydrocycloheximide, and cycloheximide isomer.

In carrying out the invention, the active material oxime advantageously is dissolved in water and the water solution sprayed on foliage of plants which it is desired to protect from fungal attack. Thus the concentration of the active material in the solution may range from around one to around 100 parts per million, or up to the solubility of the active material in water. Such solutions advantageously are prepared by dissolving the active material in a water-miscible solvent such as dimethyl-formamide, acetone, methanol, or ethanol and adding the resulting solution to the spray tank with proper stirring and agitation. By the use of such concentrated solutions in which the active material suitably can range from about one to about 25 percent or more depending upon the solubility in the solvent, the very dilute aqueous solutions which are advantageously employed according to the invention are readily prepared. A concentrate containing one percent of the active material in ethanol provides a composition which for each level teaspoon (5 cc.) per gallon give about thirteen to fourteen parts of the active material per million parts of water. Each pint per 100 gallons provides about the same concentration. Similarly a 17.5 percent solution in dimethylformamide (or acetone or methanol or ethanol) when diluted provides about thirteen to fourteen parts of the active material for each million parts of water.

2

Wetting and spreading agents can be included in the spray solutions in accordance with the usual practice in the agricultural art. Anionic, cationic and non-ionic surfactants can be used. Suitable surfactants include alkyl sulfates and sulfonates, alkylarylsulfonates, sulfosuccinate esters, polyoxyethylene sulfates, polyoxyethylene sorbitan monolaurate, alkylarylpolyether sulfates, alkylarylpolyether alcohols, alkylnaphthalene sulfonates, alkyl quaternary ammonium salts, sulfated fatty acid esters, sulfated fatty acid amides, glycerol mannitan laurate, polyalkylether condensates of fatty acids, and ligninsulfonates.

If desired, the active material can be compounded into a wettable powder. Thus the active material can be milled with an inert powder such as talc, pyrophyllite, Georgia clay, bentonite, or mixtures thereof and a wetting and dispersing material to provide a composition which is readily incorporated into a spray solution. A suitable formulation is obtained by milling and blending 434.5 pounds of Georgia clay, 4.5 pounds of Triton X–100 (an alkylarylpolyether alcohol) as a wetting agent, 9 pounds of Daxad 27 (polymerized sodium salts of substituted benzoic long chain alkyl sulfonic acid) as a dispersant, and 5.5 pounds of the active material. The resulting composition has the following percentage (by weight) composition.

	Percent
Active material	1.2
Triton X–100	1
Daxad 27	2
Georgia clay	95.8

This formulation when added to water at one pound per hundred gallons gives a spray formulation containing about 13 to 14 parts per million of the active material.

The efficacy of the compositions for the control of cherry leaf spot caused by *Coccomyces hiemalis* is illustrated in the following tables.

Young cherry trees were sprayed with aqueous solutions containing the active material in the concentrations indicated and allowed to grow for five days. After five days (A), one week (B), two weeks (C), and three weeks (D) the plants were inoculated with *Coccomyces hiemalis*.

Table I

Treatment	Leaf Spot on New Leaves—Lesions per 2 sq. in.			
	A	B	C	D
Cycloheximide oxime:				
10 p.p.m	39	-------	20	-------
30 p.p.m	-------	17	-------	20
60 p.p.m	13	4	trace	4
CONTROL				
Unsprayed	69	49	-------	39
Cycloheximide: 1 p.p.m	-------	50	83±	-------

Table II gives the comparative incidence of leaf spots on new leaves in lesions per 2 square inches for a number of the active compounds. As in the tests shown in Table I, young cherry trees were sprayed with aqueous compositions containing the active materials in the concentrations indicated and were inoculated with *Coccomyces hiemalis* after five days.

Figure 1.

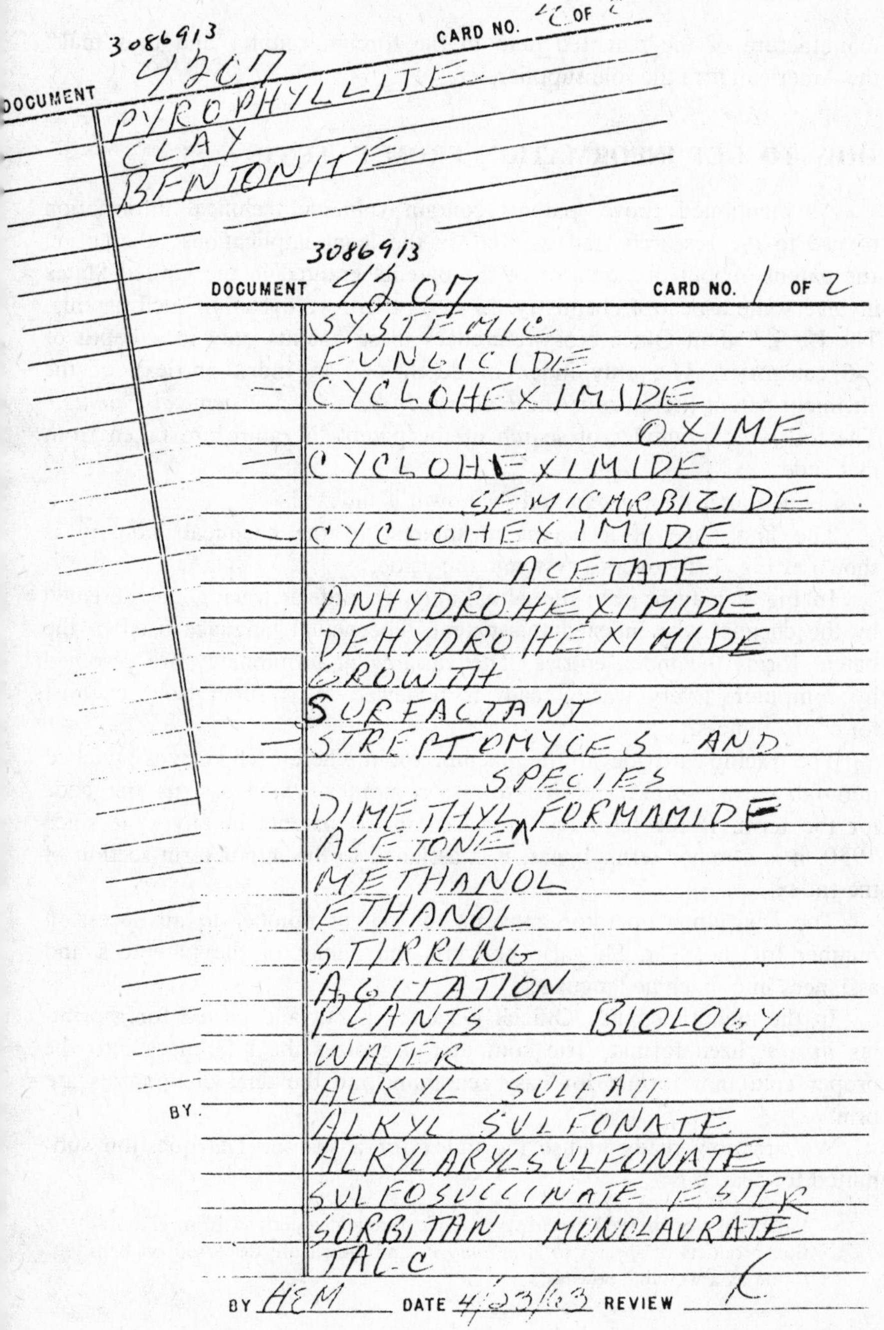

DOCUMENT 3086913 4207 CARD NO. 2 OF 2

PYROPHYLLITE
CLAY
BENTONITE

DOCUMENT 3086913 4207 CARD NO. 1 OF 2

SYSTEMIC
FUNGICIDE
— CYCLOHEXIMIDE
OXIME
— CYCLOHEXIMIDE
SEMICARBIZIDE
— CYCLOHEXIMIDE
ACETATE
ANHYDROHEXIMIDE
DEHYDROHEXIMIDE
GROWTH
SURFACTANT
— STREPTOMYCES AND
SPECIES
DIMETHYL FORMAMIDE
ACETONE
METHANOL
ETHANOL
STIRRING
AGITATION
PLANTS BIOLOGY
WATER
ALKYL SULFATE
ALKYL SULFONATE
ALKYLARYLSULFONATE
SULFOSUCCINATE ESTER
SORBITAN MONOLAURATE
TALC

BY HEM DATE 4/23/63 REVIEW

BY

Figure 2.

manufacture of the patented item in the foreign country and thus make the American firm the sole supplier.[1]

HOW TO GET INFORMATION FROM PATENTS

As mentioned above, patents contain valuable technical information of use to the research staff as well as the legal implications inherent in the patent. About one quarter of the patents granted in the United States involve some aspect of chemistry. In 1965 there were 16,048 such patents. The U. S. Patent Office cross-references these patents only to a depth of 5-6 categories. The only index in depth (40-45 index entries) of the chemical patent literature is the *Uniterm Index to U.S. Chemical Patents.*[2] The following examples of search of the patent literature are taken from that Index.

Let us start with a patent and see how it is indexed.

The first page of a patent of interest to the chemical industry is shown as Fig. 1. It covers a systemic fungicide.

In Fig. 2 may be seen the actual entry record, or tracing card, created by the chemist who indexed this patent. The actual language used in the patent forms the index entries. The variants in terminology are resolved by computer. Every tracing card is reviewed by a supervisory chemist for completeness.

The tracing card goes to the machine room where each entry is punched into tab cards, sorted and fed to the computer which assigns the code for the term. If the term has appeared in 10 patents in any year since 1950, it is a major term. If not, it is assigned to the minor term section of the Index.

The key-punch operator converts the patent number to an accession number for the year. She also converts the names of the patentees and assignees into machine language.

In the meantime, the "Official Gazette" is cut and pasted for reprinting in a stylized format. The computer organizes the references into the proper columnar format for easy searching and the dual dictionaries are printed.

We are now ready to use the index for a search. The question submitted for search is:

> Patents issued in 1963 covering systemic fungicides derived from elaboration products of species of *streptomyces* and which are dispersed on bentonite as a wettable powder.

Our search terms then are

1. systemic
2. fungicide
3. *streptomyces*
4. bentonite

Figure 3 shows the entries in the 1963 index which contain the records of patents issued during the year under each of the four search terms. Note that the accession numbers are arranged in tabular form by terminal digit. If one now matches the first two terms, two coincidental patent references are found. These two are then matched against the third term, as in Fig. 3(a), to eliminate those patents not covering elaboration products of species of *streptomyces*. There is one patent reference left. The fourth term, bentonite, is examined for this number. Only one patent granted in 1963 satisfies our search.

Fig. 4 is the page of the abstract book on which this patent is described. Note that the terms "streptomyces" and "bentonite" do not appear in the abstract. This fact indicates that these terms were picked up from the disclosure.

The cycloheximide derivatives covered by our patent are to be found in the minor terms section of the index as is shown in Fig. 5. In Fig. 6 the inventors are shown in an index of all patentees for 1963.

The table of assignees, a sample page of which is Fig. 7, is highly useful in maintaining surveillance on patents granted to various companies. Many users will check a compound in conjunction with the assignee listing to show all patents issued to a possible competitor. The patent which we illustrated was not assigned and therefore no entry appears in the assignee list.

For a detailed description of how the UNITERM INDEX TO U.S. CHEMICAL PATENTS may be searched by computer, see "Computerized Search of the U.S. Chemical Patent Literature," by Paul W. Howerton, in "Automation and Scientific Communication," American Documentation Institute, 26th Annual Meeting, October 1963.

CONCLUSION

The world's patent literature can be as valuable a source of technical information as its periodical literature. In some ways patents can be even more valuable than periodicals. For instance, the authors of scientific papers seldom chronicle their failures in the laboratory; but the patent very frequently will reveal methods tried but found less effective than the claimed method. This disclosure precludes others from entering into competition with the patent owner by applying for patent coverage of the dis-

336

FULL OIL										
	1880	2061	8482	393	54	4605		4117	2058	1729
	2060	7931		2193	8714			7827	3218	3459
	2460			3873	10024			7937	3448	7219
	3530			4233	10444			7977	3458	8959
	4640			4473	11254			10437	4878	10279
	5200			5503					5278	10289
	5420			6303					10738	12039
	6450			6383					11208	
				9173					11978	
				11123					12038	
FULLERS EARTH										
	390	551	2362	11163	3784			47	3978	1269
	3850	7221		11903	4924			1577	6398	10429
					8304			4877		
					8394					
					11314					
FULLING										
					9364	2175		2407		8949
FULLNESS										
		3671			3834		9176			
FULVENE										
					6684					10089
FUMARIC ACID, FUMARATE										
	120	741	672	1253	694	755	756	397	1998	2229
	1530	1551	3292	1993	2494	3585	1546	1027		3989
	1550	2161	3322		5414	3915	1876	1737		7239
	3050	8371	5592		7194	3935	2216	7997		7749
	5670	10301	9732		7484	5625	3296	9747		
	9840	10511	10532		8294	6325	4266	10307		
	10550		11922		9474	7095	10896			
	10750					9635	11256			
						10065	11446			
						10305				
FUME										
	6370	3901	8222	3673	3684	1745		5107	38	5079
		10221			8244	2115		8357	438	5169
					11414	4155		12097	3798	6149
						7485				6169
						8485				7919
						8825				
FUMIGATION, FUMIGANT										
	5570	1501	642		6654	8865	7106		688	9709
			6312		10784		10486		2428	
									3728	
									5338	
FUMING NITRIC ACID										
					1164		4586		258	219
					9904				5488	
FUNGI, FUNGUS										
	3950	351	6932	1503	4444	2165	2426	1587	108	3519
	6140	641	7192	1713	4704	2565	4926	2267	1508	7729
	9250	651	7352	5093	5574	4445	10006	3277	4928	11849
	9610	951	8162	5133	7294	5575		8697	6458	
	12130	7741	8602	5803	10254	6655		10007	7278	
		7851				8145		12117	10538	
						8215				
						8525				
FUNGICIDE, FUNGISTATIC										
	1230	941	492	783	1094	345	1116	1757	108	349
	1900	1591	642	1233	1904	805	2426	2247	1968	689
	2820	1901	2302	3103	2374	1115	3526	2427	3728	1229
	3110	2421	2422	4273	2724	2265	3726	2717	3988	1969
	5570	3101	2822	5093	3114	2565	4926	4207	4928	1989
	5860	3271	3102	5413	3594	3725	5126	5867	6138	2292
	6400	4531	4202	5983	3724	5195	7016	5927	8388	2719
	7190	4661	4282	7193	4044	5575	8036	6137	9048	3109
	7820	4741	4532	7443	5004	6135	8526	6657	9478	3519
	8740	5981	4802	7873	5214	6205	9496	7287	11218	3729
	10250	6461	6932	8043	6004	6485	10246	7707	11528	4439
		8581	7192	8183	6654	6655	11216	9497	11938	5389
		8811	7502	8753	6934	8185	11466	10587	12238	7189
		9241	7732	9433	7294	8335	12236	11217		8389
		10111	8602	10333	7724	8525				9509
		11771	9122	11063	7734					11299
			9132	11283	8244					12239
			9662	11523	8434					
			9982		9104					
			10842		10854					
			11222		11064					
			11292							

*SYNTHETIC SEE SYNTHESIS

SYNTHETIC RESIN, 11364, 11591

*SYNTHETIC RUBBER SEE RUBBER

SYPHACIA AND SPECIES, 1330, 3939

SYPHON, 7936

SYSTEMIC, 2719, 3522, 4207, 9610

SYSTOLIC, 4934

SYTON W-20, 1740

*TABULAR ALUMINA SEE ALPHA-ALUMINA

TABUN SEE ETHYL DIMETHYL PHOSPHOROEMIDOCYANIDATE

*TACK-FREE SEE NONTACKY

*TACKIFIER SEE TACKY

*TACKINESS SEE TACKY

TACK WELDING, 4229

TACOL 2, 11723

TAENIA AND SPECIES, 944

TAIL, 843, 1893, 3929, 4117, 7594

TAKADIASTASE, 6145

TAKE-UP, 5902, 11444

TAKE-UP ROLL, 11209

*TALCUM SEE TALC

*TALLATE SEE TALL OIL

*TALL OIL ACID SEE TALL OIL FATTY ACID

*TALL OIL ESTER SEE TALL OIL

TALL OIL PITCH, 10298

TALL OIL-POLYPROPYLENE OXIDE ADDUCT, 10537

TALL OIL SOAP, 10464

*TALLOL SEE TALL OIL

TALLOW ALCOHOL, 1550, 5000, 5647

TALLOW AMINE, 1086, 1921, 5199, 5200, 11261

TALLOW AMINE ACETATE, 2703

N-TALLOW-BETA-AMINOPROPIONIC ACID, 8544

3-TALLOWAMINOPROPYLAMINE, 11843

TALLOW DIAMINE, 11480

TALLOW DIETHANOLAMINE, 1086

N-TALLOW N,N,N',N',N'-PENTAMETHYL-1,3-PROPYLENEDIAMMONIUM CHLORIDE, 8482

N-TALLOW PROPYLENE DIAMINE N-COCO-BETA-AMINOPROPIONATE, 8544

TALLOWTRIMETHYLAMMONIUM CHLORIDE, 1927

TALLOYL AMIDES, 6976

TALUS SLOPE, 898

TAMOL, 5885, 10313, 10802

TANDEM, 11378

TANG, 3194

TANGLE, 3428

*TANKER SEE TANK

TANNAGE, 8816

TANNATE, 9956, 11176

Figure 3.

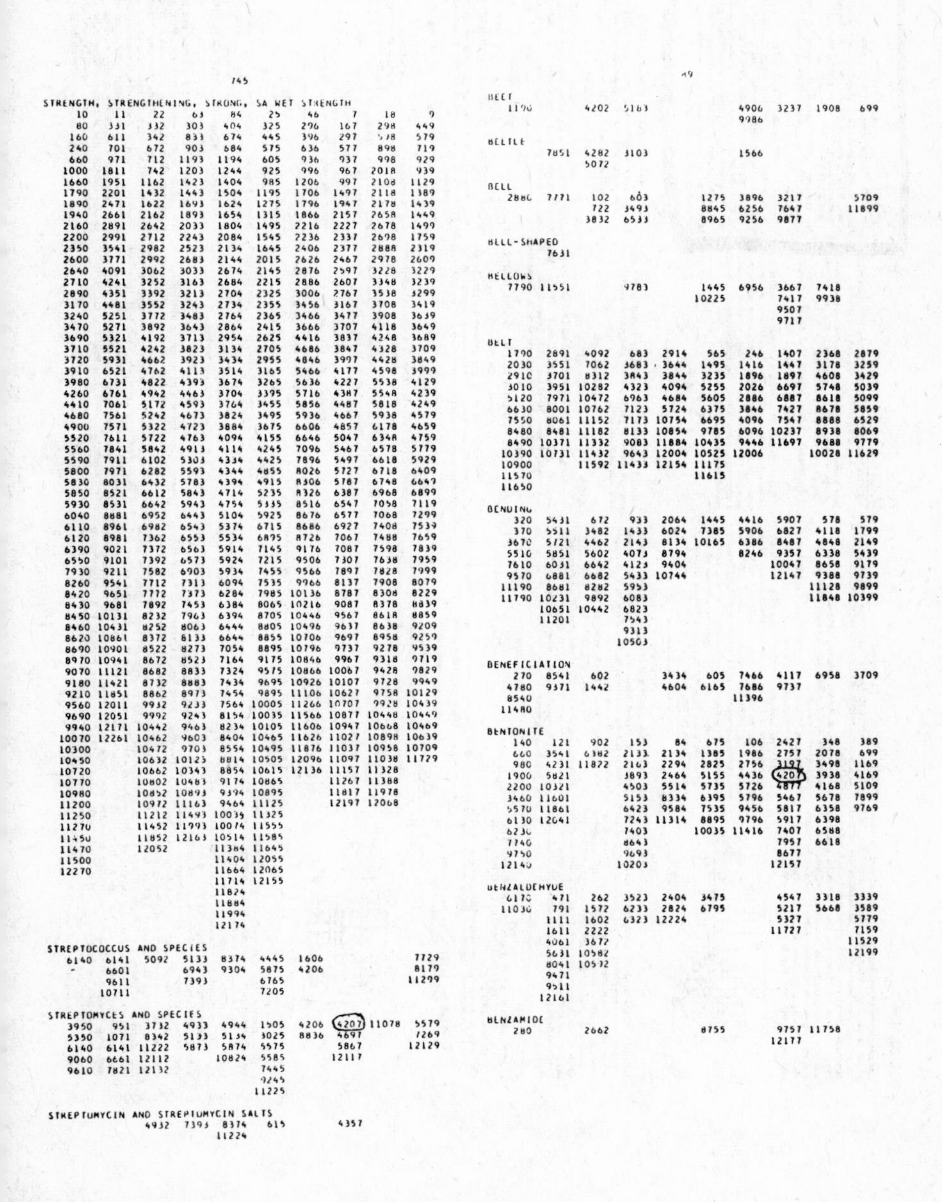

745

STRENGTH, STRENGTHENING, STRONG, SA WET STRENGTH

10	11	22	63	84	25	46	7	18	9
80	331	332	303	404	325	296	167	298	449
160	611	342	833	674	445	396	297	578	579
240	701	672	903	684	575	636	577	898	719
660	971	712	1193	1194	605	936	937	998	929
1000	1811	742	1203	1244	925	996	967	2018	939
1660	1951	1162	1423	1404	985	1206	997	2108	1129
1790	2201	1432	1443	1504	1195	1706	1497	2118	1389
1890	2471	1622	1693	1624	1275	1796	1947	2178	1439
1940	2661	2162	1893	1654	1315	1866	2157	2658	1449
2160	2891	2642	2033	1804	1495	2216	2227	2678	1499
2200	2991	2712	2243	2084	1545	2236	2337	2698	1759
2350	3541	2982	2523	2134	1645	2406	2377	2888	2319
2600	3771	2992	2683	2144	2015	2626	2467	2978	2609
2640	4091	3062	3033	2674	2145	2876	2597	3228	3229
2710	4241	3252	3163	2684	2215	2886	2607	3348	3239
2890	4351	3392	3213	2704	2325	3006	2767	3538	3299
3170	4481	3552	3243	2734	2355	3456	3167	3708	3419
3240	5251	3772	3483	2764	2365	3466	3477	3908	3639
3470	5271	3892	3643	2864	2415	3666	3707	4118	3649
3690	5321	4192	3713	2954	2625	4416	3837	4248	3689
3710	5521	4242	3823	3134	2705	4686	3847	4328	3709
3720	5931	4662	3923	3434	2955	4846	3997	4428	3849
3910	6521	4762	4113	3514	3165	5466	4177	4598	3999
3980	6731	4822	4393	3674	3265	5636	4227	5538	4129
4260	6761	4942	4463	3704	3395	5716	4387	5548	4239
4410	7061	5172	4593	3764	3455	5856	4487	5818	4249
4680	7561	5242	4673	3824	3495	5936	4667	5938	4579
4900	7571	5322	4723	3884	3675	6606	4857	6178	4659
5520	7611	5722	4763	4094	4155	6646	5047	6348	4759
5560	7841	5842	4913	4114	4245	7096	5467	6578	5779
5590	7911	6102	5303	4334	4425	7896	5497	6618	5929
5800	7971	6282	5593	4344	4855	8026	5727	6718	6409
5830	8031	6432	5783	4394	4915	8306	5787	6748	6647
5850	8521	6612	5843	4714	5235	8326	6387	6968	6899
5930	8531	6642	5943	4754	5335	8516	6547	7058	7119
6040	8881	6952	6443	5104	5925	8676	6577	7068	7299
6110	8961	6982	6543	5374	6715	8686	6927	7408	7539
6120	8981	7362	6553	5534	6875	8726	7067	7488	7659
6390	9021	7372	6563	5914	7145	9176	7087	7598	7839
6550	9101	7392	6573	5924	7215	9506	7307	7638	7959
7930	9211	7582	6903	5934	7455	9566	7897	7828	7999
8260	9541	7712	7313	6094	7535	9966	8137	7908	8079
8420	9651	7772	7373	6284	7985	10136	8787	8308	8229
8430	9681	7892	7453	6384	8065	10216	9087	8378	8839
8450	10131	8232	7963	6394	8705	10446	9567	8618	8859
8460	10431	8252	8063	6444	8805	10496	9637	8638	9209
8620	10861	8372	8133	6644	8855	10706	9697	8958	9259
8690	10901	8522	8273	7054	8895	10796	9737	9278	9539
8970	10941	8672	8523	7164	9175	10846	9967	9318	9719
9070	11121	8682	8833	7324	9575	10866	10067	9428	9829
9180	11421	8732	8883	7434	9695	10926	10107	9728	9949
9210	11851	8862	8973	7454	9895	11106	10627	9758	10129
9560	12011	9932	9233	7564	10005	11266	10707	9928	10439
9690	12051	9992	9243	8154	10035	11566	10877	10448	10449
9940	12171	10442	9463	8234	10105	11606	10947	10668	10469
10070	12261	10462	9603	8404	10465	11626	11027	10898	10639
10300		10472	9703	8554	10495	11876	11037	10958	10709
10450		10632	10123	8814	10505	12096	11097	11038	11729
10720		10662	10343	8854	10615	12136	11157	11328	
10770		10802	10483	9174	10865		11267	11388	
10980		10852	10893	9394	10895		11817	11978	
11200		10972	11163	9464	11125		12197	12068	
11250		11212	11493	10035	11325				
11270		11452	11793	10074	11555				
11450		11852	12163	10514	11585				
11470		12052		11384	11645				
11500				11404	12055				
12270				11664	12065				
				11714	12155				
				11824					
				11884					
				11994					
				12174					

STREPTOCOCCUS AND SPECIES

6140	6141	5092	5133	8374	4445	1606			7729
-	6601		6943	9304	5875	4206			8179
	9611		7393		6765				11299
	10711				7205				

STREPTOMYCES AND SPECIES

3950	951	3732	4933	4944	1505	4206	4207	11078	5579
5350	1071	8342	5133	5134	3025	8836	4697		7269
6140	6141	11222	5873	5874	5575		5867		12129
9060	6661	12112		10824	5585		12117		
9610	7821	12132			7445				
					9245				
					11225				

STREPTOMYCIN AND STREPTOMYCIN SALTS

		4932	7393	8374	615		4357		
				11224					

49

BEET

1190		4202	5183			4906	3237	1908	699
						9986			

BEETLE

	7851	4282	3103			1566			
		5072							

BELL

2880	7771	102	603		1275	3896	3217		5709
		722	3493		8845	6256	7647		11899
		3832	6533		8965	9256	9877		

BELL-SHAPED

	7631								

BELLOWS

7790	11551		9783		1445	6956	3667	7418	
					10225		7417	9938	
							9507		
							9717		

BELT

1790	2891	4092	683	2914	565	246	1407	2368	2879
2030	3551	7062	3683	3644	1495	1416	1447	3178	3259
2910	3701	8312	3843	3844	3235	1896	1897	4608	3429
3010	3951	10282	4323	4094	5255	2026	6697	5748	5039
5120	7971	10472	6963	4684	5605	2886	6887	8618	5099
6630	8001	10762	7123	5724	6375	3846	7427	8678	5859
7550	8061	11152	7173	10754	6695	4096	7547	8888	6529
8480	8481	11182	8133	10854	9785	6096	10237	8938	8069
8490	10371	11332	9083	11884	10435	9446	11697	9688	9779
10390	10731	11432	9643	12004	10525	12006		10028	11629
10900		11592	11433	12154	11175				
11570					11615				
11650									

BENDING

320	5431	672	933	2064	1445	4416	5907	578	579
370	5511	3482	1433	6024	7385	5906	6827	4118	1799
3670	5721	4462	2143	8134	10165	6386	8487	4848	2149
5510	5851	5602	4073	8794		8246	9357	6338	5439
7610	6031	6642	4123	9404			10047	8658	9179
9570	6881	6682	5433	10744			12147	9388	9739
11190	8681	8282	5953					11128	9899
11790	10231	9892	6083					11848	10399
	10651	10442	6823						
	11201		7543						
			9313						
			10503						

BENEFICIATION

270	8541	602		3434	605	7466	4117	6958	3709
4780	9371	1442		4604	6165	7686	9737		
8540						11396			
11480									

BENTONITE

140	121	902	153	84	675	106	2427	348	389
660	3541	6382	2133	2134	1385	1986	2757	2078	699
980	4231	11872	2163	2294	2825	2756	3197	3498	1169
1900	5821		3893	2464	5155	4436	4207	3938	4169
2200	10321		4503	5514	5735	5726	4877	4168	5109
3460	11601		5153	8334	6395	5796	5467	5678	7899
5570	11861		6423	9584	7535	9456	5817	6358	9769
6130	12041		7243	11314	8895	9796	5917	6398	
6230			7403		10035	11416	7407	6588	
7740			8643				7957	6618	
9750			9693				8677		
12140			10203				12157		

BENZALDEHYDE

6170	471	262	3523	2404	3475		4547	3318	3339
11030	791	1572	6233	2824	6795		5217	5668	3589
	1111	1602	6323	12224			5327		5779
	1611	2222					11727		7159
	4061	3672							11529
	5631	10582							12199
	8041	10572							
	9471								
	9511								
	12161								

BENZAMIDE

280		2662			8755		9757	11758	
							12177		

Figure 3a.

APRIL 23, 1963

laminate is cooled, the improvement in applying the laminating pressure comprising disposing the metal strip and the organic film between a pair of substantially parallel opposing surfaces, one of the opposing surfaces being relatively firm and unyielding and the other being relatively soft and yielding under the laminating pressure, the soft and yielding opposing surface being formed of a rubbery polymer having a hardness not greater than about 55 durometers, the relatively firm and unyielding opposing

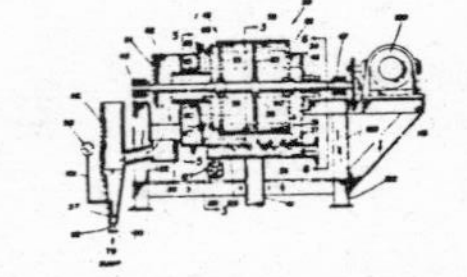

surface having a hardness substantially greater than the soft and yielding opposing surface, and applying laminating pressure to the metal strip and organic film with the opposing surfaces, the relatively soft and yielding opposing surface applying pressure to the organic film and the relatively firm and unyielding opposing surface applying pressure to the side of the metal strip opposite the side having the adhesive coated surface area with organic film thereon.

4199 **3,086,905**

APPARATUS AND PROCESS FOR CONTINUOUSLY TESTING AND CONTROLLING STOCK FREENESS

Cloyd B. Richardson, Chillicothe, Ohio, assignor to The Mead Corporation, Dayton, Ohio, a corporation of Ohio

Filed Dec. 11, 1958, Ser. No. 779,637
10 Claims. (Cl. 162—198)

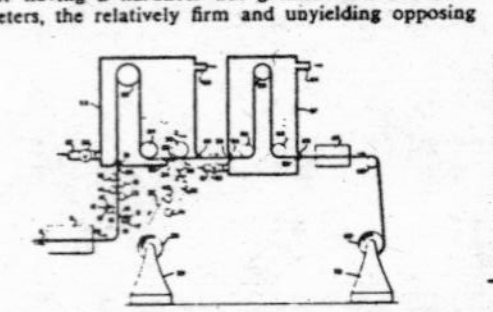

10. A process for continuously testing and controlling the freeness of paper stock material comprising the steps of diverting a substantially continuous flow of paper stock from a stock refining apparatus to a container at a rate to maintain a relatively high constant level of stock therein, rotating a peripherally perforated filtering drum about a horizontally disposed axis within the paper stock in said container thereby forming a mat of fibers on the outer surface of said filtering drum as fluid from said stock filters through said mat into said filtering drum, maintaining a relatively low constant level of fluid in said filtering drum by gravity overflow therefrom under constant pressure conditions, measuring the rate of flow of said fluid through said mat to determine the freeness of said stock, and regulating said stock refining apparatus in accordance with the determined freeness of said stock, said relatively high and low levels being respectively considerably above and below said axis.

4200 **3,086,906**

DINITRO PHENOL AND DINITRO NAPHTHOL ALKANOLAMINE SALT PESTICIDAL COMPOSITIONS

Louis Werotte, Boitsfort, Belgium, assignor to Poudreries Reunies de Belgique Soc. An., Brussels, Belgium, a corporation of Belgium

No Drawing. Filed Sept. 26, 1955, Ser. No. 536,730
6 Claims. (Cl. 167—31)

1. The pesticidal composition comprising the di-ethanolamine salt of 2,4-dinitro phenol, mono-sodium phosphate, and sodium dodecyl benzene sulfonate, said compounds being intimately mixed with each other, the mono-sodium phosphate and the sodium dodecyl benzene sulfonate being present in said composition in an amount sufficient to impart to a 1.5% aqueous solution of said composition a pH of about 6.3 and a surface tension of about 31 dynes per cm. at 18° C.

4201 **3,086,907**

METHOD FOR CONTROLLING SOIL NEMATODES

Frederick A. Hessel, Montclair, N.J., assignor to General Aniline & Film Corporation, New York, N.Y., a corporation of Delaware

No Drawing. Filed Mar. 6, 1958, Ser. No. 719,520
3 Claims. (Cl. 167—33)

1. A process of controlling and eradicating nematodes from nematode infested soil which comprises introducing to the soil a nematocidal amount of a nematocide having the following general formula:

wherein R represents a member selected from the class consisting of oxygen and imino group.

4202 **3,086,908**

FUNGICIDAL COPPER SPRAYS

Otto Telle and Ferdinand Grewe, Cologne-Stammheim, Germany, assignors to Farbenfabriken Bayer Aktiengesellschaft, Leverkusen, Germany, a corporation of Germany

No Drawing. Filed May 27, 1958, Ser. No. 738,017
Claims priority, application Germany June 7, 1957
6 Claims. (Cl. 167—42)

1. Fungicidal copper sprays containing a mixture of
(A) a fatty alcohol polyglycol ether,
(B) a fatty acid metal salt, and
(C) a fungicidal copper compound with a copper content (referred to metallic copper) from 5 to 70%.

4203 **3,086,909**

THERAPEUTIC COMPOSITION OF LITHOSPERMUM ERYTHRORHIZON IN JAPAN WAX AND SESAME OIL

Kinzo Otsuki and Junzo Otsuki, both of 18 Kami-Koya, Fukuchiyama, Kyoto, Japan

No Drawing. Filed Sept. 28, 1960, Ser. No. 58,884
4 Claims. (Cl. 167—58)

1. A therapeutically useful ointment consisting predominantly of a base constituted by a thermal blend of Japan wax and sesame oil, and containing a minor proportion of a therapeutically active ingredient, said ointment base having an acid value of 5.4, a saponification value of 186.4, an iodine value of 85.2 and a melting range of 38–41° C. and including 2.56% by weight of unsaponifiables.

4204 **3,086,910**

CENTRAL NERVOUS SYSTEM DEPRESSANTS 3-(2'-PYRIDYL)-4-QUINAZOLONES

Jola Vithal Shetty, Liborio A. Campanella, and Edwin Hays, Rochester, N.Y., assignors to Wallace & Tiernan Inc., a corporation of Delaware

No Drawing. Filed Mar. 9, 1960, Ser. No. 13,692
3 Claims. (Cl. 167—65)

1. The method of treating a patient who suffers from increased nervous tension to an excessive or abnormal degree to relieve such tension which comprises administering to the patient a therapeutically effective amount of a compound selected from the group consisting of compounds of the general formula:

where R is selected from the group consisting of hydrogen and lower alkyls; and their pharmaceutically acceptable acid addition salts.

4205 **3,086,911**

ANALGESIC: 3,4-DIMETHYLBENZAMIDE

Bernard Beau Brown, Westfield, and William Glen Bywater, Upper Montclair, N.J., assignors to S. B. Penick and Company, New York, N.Y., a corporation of Delaware

No Drawing. Filed May 26, 1961, Ser. No. 112,776
5 Claims. (Cl. 167—65)

1. The method of mitigating protopathic pain in animals which comprises the oral administration of 3,4-dimethylbenzamide to an animal having protopathic pain.

4206 **3,086,912**

ANTIBIOTIC LINCOLNENSIN AND METHOD OF PRODUCTION

Malcolm E. Bergy and Ross R. Herr, Kalamazoo, Mich., and Donald Joseph Mason, Portage Township, Kalamazoo County, Mich., assignors to The Upjohn Company, Kalamazoo, Mich., a corporation of Delaware

Filed July 3, 1961, Ser. No. 121,696
10 Claims. (Cl. 167—65)

1. A composition of matter assaying at least 20 mcg. per mg. of lincolnensin selected from the group consisting of
(1) lincolnensin free base, a basic substance characterized by
(*a*) being monobasic and having an equivalent weight of 454.7 and a pKa' of about 7.6,
(*b*) having no UV absorption maxima from 220 to 400 millimicrons,
(*c*) a calculated molecular formula of

$$C_{18}H_{34}N_2O_6S$$

and, in the form of its crystalline hydrochloride by
(*d*) characteristic infrared absorption in mineral oil mull at the following frequencies expressed in reciprocal centimeters: 3340, 3240, 3150, 3080, 2930, 2850, 2160, 1690, 1675, 1600, 1590, 1450, 1375, 1315, 1305, 1276, 1265, 1233, 1185, 1155, 1140, 1115, 1100, 1093, 1078, 1042, 1006, 990, 985, 970, 924, 906, 875, 855, 827, 793, 717, 690, and
(2) the acid addition salts thereof.

4207 **3,086,913**

SYSTEMIC FUNGICIDES

James M. Hamilton, 574 S. Main St., and Michael Szkolnik, R.D. 2, both of Geneva, N.Y., and Ernest Sondheimer, Geneva, N.Y. (956 Westmoreland Ave., Syracuse 10, N.Y.)

No Drawing. Continuation of application Ser. No. 615,752, Oct. 15, 1956. This application Apr. 27, 1962, Ser. No. 190,767
6 Claims. (Cl. 167—65)

1. A process for controlling fungal diseases of plants which comprises applying to the plant a compound that translocates systemically in the plant to growth developing after the application of the compound to the plant whereby protection of post-application new growth as well as old growth is obtained, said compound being selected from the group consisting of cycloheximide oxime and cycloheximide semicarbazone.

4208 **3,086,914**

LIP-COLORING COMPOSITIONS

Saul Soloway, New Rochelle, N.Y., assignor to Faberge, Inc., Ridgefield, N.J., a corporation of New York

No Drawing. Filed June 23, 1959, Ser. No. 822,196
7 Claims. (Cl. 167—85)

1. A lip-coloring composition containing waxes, oils, a dye selected from the class consisting of fluoran and xanthene dyes, and an amide solvent selected from the class consisting of N-methyl acetamide, N-2-hydroxyethyl acetamide and N,N-dimethyl acetamide.

4209 **3,086,915**

NON-DELIQUESCENT VITAMIN C CONCENTRATE

Philip Morse, La Habra, Calif., assignor to Nutrilite Products, Inc., Buena Park, Calif., a corporation of California

No Drawing. Filed Aug. 7, 1961, Ser. No. 129,557
11 Claims. (Cl. 195—2)

1. A process for producing a non-deliquescent powder from the juice of acerola cherry which comprises adding to said juice a base selected from the group consisting of the oxides, hydroxides, and carbonates of an alkaline earth metal, sodium hydroxide and sodium carbonate, and mixtures thereof, to a pH of about 4.5 to about 8.0 removing the precipitate formed and subjecting the clear liquid to a drying step to produce a dry, substantially non-deliquescent powder.

4210 **3,086,916**

PROCESS FOR PRODUCING L-GLUTAMIC ACID FROM RACEMIC GLUTAMIC ACID

Shukuo Kinoshita, Masao Tanaka, and Yo Kato, Tokyo, Japan, assignors to Kyowa Hakko Kogyo Co., Ltd., Tokyo, Japan, a corporation of Japan

No Drawing. Filed Aug. 2, 1961, Ser. No. 128,695
12 Claims. (Cl. 195—29)

1. A process for producing L-glutamic acid from racemic glutamic acid, which comprises adding an enzymatic material produced by cultivation of a glutamic acid-racemase-yielding bacteria belonging to Lactobacillus group and an enzymatic material produced by cultivation of a strain of *Pseudomonas cruciviae* (including its mutant strains) to an aqueous solution containing racemic glutamic acid, thereby causing a reaction to convert the glutamic acid to L-2-pyrrolidone-carboxylic acid, and hydrolyzing the resulting L-pyrrolidone-5-carboxylic acid, and recovering L-glutamic acid from the hydrolysate.

Nos. 4199 - 4210

Figure 4.

188

CYCLOHEXENE-1-CARBOXALDEHYDE, 4934

3-CYCLOHEXENE-1-CARBOXAMIDE, 4792

3-CYCLOHEXENE-1-CARBOXYLIC ACID, 4792

CYCLOHEXENE CHLORIDE, 6016

1-CYCLOHEXENE-1,2-DICARBOXIMIDES, 2805

CIS-4-CYCLOHEXENE-1,2-DICARBOXYLIC ACID ANHYDRIDE, 3779

4-CYCLOHEXENE-1,2-DICARBOXYLIC ACID ANHYDRIDE, 6614

•4-CYCLOHEXENE-1,2-DICARBOXYLIC ACID SEE TETRAHYDROPHTHALIC ACID

CYCLOHEXENE HYDROPEROXIDE, 6794

CYCLOHEXENE OXIDE, 3754, 10027, 10844, 11294, 12180

CYCLOHEXENOL, 3804, 6794, 11075

/2,3/-CYCLOHEX-4'-EN-3-ONE ANDROSTAN-3-ONES, 1763

2-CYCLOHEXENONE, 1763

1-CYCLOHEXENYL(AMINO)METHANES, 10319

3-CYCLOHEXENYL-8,9-(1,'3'-BUTADIEN-1,4-YLENE)-2-OXOBENZQUINOLIZINES, 2261

2-CYCLOHEXENYL-N-(2'-CHLOROALLYL)-3-METHOXYPROPYLDITHIOCARBAMATE, 1964

2-CYCLOHEXENYL 2-CYANOETHYLDITHIOCARBAMATE, 3109

2-CYCLOHEXENYL 2-CYCLOHEXENYLDITHIOCARBAMATE, 3109

1-(1'-CYCLOHEXENYL)DIETHYLAMINO-4-PHENYLBUTANE, 10319

2-CYCLOHEXENYL DIETHYLDITHIOCARBAMATE, 1964

2-CYCLOHEXENYL DIMETHYLDITHIOCARBAMATE, 1964

CYCLOHEXENYL DITHIOCARAMATES, 1964

2-CYCLOHEXENYL DITHIOCARBAMATE, 3109

2-CYCLOHEXENYL-5-ETHYL-2-METHYL-1-PIPERIDINECARBODITHIOATE, 1964

1-CYCLOHEXENYL FLUORIDE, 6016

N-CYCLOHEXENYLFORMAMIDE, 7739

CYCLOHEXENYL-(3)HYDROGEN PEROXIDE, 6794

2-CYCLOHEXENYL ISO-OCTYLDITHIOCARBAMATE, 3109

2-CYCLOHEXENYL 2-METHALLYLDITHIOCARBAMATE, 3109

3-CYCLOHEXENYLMETHYL BIS(2-ETHYLHEXYL)1,2,4-BUTANETRICARBOXYLATE, 1093

3-CYCLOHEXENYLMETHYL BIS(OXO PROCESS DECYL)1,2,4-BUTANETRICARBOXYLATE, 1093

5-DELTA'-CYCLOHEXENYL-5-METHYL N-METHYL-BARBITURIC ACID, 2435

2-CYCLOHEXENYL-1-PIPERIDINECARBODITHIOATE, 1964

2-CYCLOHEXENYL-1-PYRROLIDINECARBODITHIOATE, 1964

2-CYCLOHEXENYL-1,2,3,6-TETRAHYDROPYRIDINECARBODITHIOATE, 1964

CYCLOHEXENYLTRICHLOROSILANE, 1303

CYCLOHEXIMIDE, 951, 5575, 9122

CYCLOHEXIMIDE ACETATE, 4207

CYCLOHEXIMIDE OXIME, 4207

CYCLOHEXIMIDE SEMICARBAZIDE, 4207

CYCLOHEXYLACETYLFERROCENE, 7735

CYCLOHEXYL ACRYLATE, 5166, 8316

2-CYCLOHEXYL-3-ALKYLMORPHOLINES, 1040

CYCLOHEXYL N-ALLYL-N-N-PROPYLTHIOCARBAMATE, 8106

Figure 5.

58

Name	Numbers
HAMILL, GORDON B.	6830
HAMILL, JAMES J.	2482
HAMILTON, FRANCIS W.	11847
HAMILTON, GENE E.	5421
HAMILTON, HERBERT D.	8847
HAMILTON, JAMES M.	4207
HAMILTON, PAUL M.	6108 11914
HAMILTON, ROBERT M.	4419
HAMILTON, RUSSELL	11464
HAMILTON, WILLIAM F.	3448 9624
HAMILTON, WILLIAM P.	6351 7945 8295 8495
	9017
HAMITER, WILLIAM L.	9976
HAMLIN JR., CHAUNCEY J.	3831
HAMLIN, JAMES SAMUEL	4322
HAMLIN, JERRY F.	3720
HAMM, FRANK A.	4449
HAMM, FRANKLIN A.	3734
HAMMANN WILLIAM C.	2469
HAMMEL, DAVID R.	747 2776 11022
HAMMELL, KEMPER M.	10889
HAMMER, FRANK E.	6355
HAMMERBERG, EDGAR S.	1112 3351
HAMMOND, GILBERT P.	9932
HAMMOND, JOHN E.	7571
HAMNER, GLEN PORTER	4467 5152
HAMRICK, JOSEPH T.	2636 8241 8242
HAMSAG-GARSHANIN, XENIA	9684
HAMSAG, ERNEST	9684
HANCE, CHARLES R.	2125
HANCOCK, JAMES L.	8065
HANCOCK, ROBERT D.	9596
HANDEL, NEIL E.	6264
HANDELMAN, EILEEN T.	3716
HANDLEY, MELVIN F.	2946
HANDWERK, ERWIN C.	8986
HANDWERK, GLENN E.	2104
HANEGRAAF, JOHANNES ANDREAS	11065
HANEY, STANLEY C.	4640
HANGANUTIU, MARIUS	11477
HANHART, WALTER	1957
HANINK, DEAN K.	2608
HANISIAN, JOHN	6691
HANKEY, ERNEST H.	3765
HANKS, GALE S.	5052
HANLEIN, WALTER	97
HANLON, JOSEPH F.	2871
HANLON, PATRICK G.	6277
HANN, DOUGLAS GRAEME	7301
HANN, PAUL D.	1868 2012 6801
HANNA, DELBERT L.	819
HANNON, BRUCE M.	11558
HANNON, GILBERT H.	9764
HANOTIER, JACQUES DANIEL VICTOR	1360
HANOVER, KENNETH A.	10097
HANSEN, ANDRE M.	10670 11020
HANSEN, DONALD J.	7211
HANSEN, ERLING	1523
HANSEN, GEORGE R.	5735
HANSEN, JOHN R.	6516
HANSEN, LEON C.	3266
HANSEN, ODD A.	3190
HANSEN, WALDEMAR H.	1391
HANSFORD, DAVID L.	8089
HANSFORD, ROWLAND C.	4733
HANSHAW, ELLSWORTH S.	5452
HANSJOSTEN, NIKOLAUS	3179
HANSLEY, VIRGIL L.	4141
HANSON, ALDEN W.	8807
HANSON, THOMAS P.	8247
HANSON, VICTOR GEORGE	7647
HANUS, EDWARD J.	12114
HANUSCH, HUGO	9544
HANZEL, RICHARD W.	5053
HAP, HEINZ	8800
HAPPE, RALPH A.	10642
HAPPICH, WILLIAM F.	8816
HARACZ, EDWARD F.	7405
HARADA, KAORU	1549
HARADA, KYOEI	10311
HARBIT, KEITH B.	9776
HARDESTY, ETHRIDGE E.	7816
HARDING, ARTHUR J. I.	3299
HARDISON, LESLIE C.	11673
HARDMAN, ALBERT F.	4022
HARDMAN, HARLEY F.	6107
HARDNESS	5722
HARDT, PAUL ERNST	7389
HARDWICK, WILLIAM A.	4891
HARDY JR., ROBERT ALLIS	469 521
HARDY, DENIS GEOFFREY	9841
HARDY, EDGAR F.	3987 5906
HARDY, JOHN F.	1199 1200

145

Name	Numbers
SWINCICKI, KONRAD	7005
SWINEHART, RICHARD W.	6171
SWITZER, ROBERT L.	633 8991
SYDOW, THOMAS K.	9675
SYMBOLIK, WILLIAM S.	2599
SYMES, RICHARD T.	5734
SYMES, WILLIAM F.	10048
SYRACUSE, FELIX L.	7659
SZABO, JORGE L.	10510
SZABO, KAROLY	808 7187 7977 9045
	9434 9509 9572
SZCZEPANEK, ALFRED	513
SZCZEPANEK, MARGARETE NEE SCHNOOR	513
SZCZESNIAK, ALINA S.	5807
SZECHTMAN, JOSHUA	8878
SZERENYI, ANDREW S.	7315
SZILARD, LEO	8703
SZKOLNIK, MICHAEL	4207
SZMUSZKOVICZ, JACOB	9846 10082
SZONYI, GEZA	11522
SZPILFOGEL, STEFAN ANTONI	11065
SZUEHMAN, RAUL	6651
SZUMSKI, JOHN P.	7920
TABACHNICK, HOWARD	10526
TABET, GEORGES E.	4753
TABIKH, ALI A.	1131
TACHIKI, KENKICHI	9725
TAFT, WILLIAM K.	6011
TAJIMA, SHIGERU	2222
TAKADA, KOJI	3283
TAKAGI, HISAO	11648
TAKAHASHI, MASAO	9458
TAKAHASHI, SHIRO	789
TAKAHASHI, SHIZUO	9701
TAKAHASHI, TORIZO	1603
TAKAHASHI, TORU	5215
TAKAHASHI, TOSHIO	1898
TAKAMATSU, HIDEJI	10588
TAKAMIZAWA, HIDEO	9458
TAKAMIZAWA, MINORU	10093
TAKAO, ZENICHIRO	10735
TAKASHIMA, THOMAS T.	9732
TAKAYAMA, GOZO	6453
TAKEDA, KENICHI	11043
TAKEO, KENJI	1183
TAKEUCHI, SHOICHI	6859
TALAAT, MOSTAFA E.	12077
TALBOTT, EDMOND LOWELL	12138
TALBOYS, HENRY H.	8117
TALLET, JOSEPH	2465
TALLEY, ROBERT M.	12170
TALLIS, ERNEST E.	10368
TALLMAN, CHARLES V.	10670
TALLMAN, RALPH C.	9873 9874
TAMA, MARIO	4573
TAMAGAWA, YOSHIO	10760
TAMBLYN, JOHN W.	1205 2981 6902 7958
	7959
TAMBORSKI, CHRIST	2280 8757
TAMM, CHRISTOPH	768 2510
TAMM, RUDOLF	10458
TAMMINEN, PENTTI JUUSE	1406
TAMUKI, TEIKICHI	7715
TAMURA, KIHACHI	10093
TANABE, KENICHI	32 2330 2355 6305
	9102
TANABE, MASATO	12199
TANAKA, KATSUNOBU	4211
TANAKA, KUNIYOSHI	2245
TANAKA, MASAO	4210
TANAKA, YUKIO	6639 7655
TANASESCU, DUMITRU	11477
TANCHUK, NICHOLAS R.	6376
TANCZYN, HARRY	63 3228
TANENBAUM, MORRIS	1491 3985 7645
TANG, HAMBURG	7605
TANIMURA, KATSUO	2397
TANNER, DAVID	4616 5068 5541 7697
	8118
TANNER, HERBERT GILES	5994
TANNER, MAURICE CHARLES	4873 6873
TANSEY, ROBERT P.	8136
TANTALUM OXARVIN B.	5379
TANTRAM, ANTHONY DESMOND SHAND	7653 8128
TAPAS, JOHN C.	7237
TAPPAN, GENE F.	6708
TARASEVICH, MICHAEL	6031
TARASOV, ARTHUR	10252
TARDY, PIERRE ANTHELME	3632
TARKINGTON, TERRY W.	4757
TARKOEY, NIKLAUS	507
TARLTON, EDWARD J.	10837
TARLTON, EDWARD JAMES	8216

Figure 6.

```
ARGUS CHEMICAL CORPORATION
        7691

ARKANSAS COMPANY, INC.
  870

ARMCO STELL CORPORATION
 10950  3841  6122    63  1634  2955 10736         3228 12089
        7971         923        3505
                                5115
                               11875

ARMOUR AND COMPANY
   950   651   652  2763  2354   605  1316  3937  4888  1399
  2670  3241  1112 10653  6964 11845  7466        5198  5529
  5530  3351             11844                    5528  5679
  5990 11261                                     11698 10119
  6890                                                10409

ARMOUR PHARMACEUTICAL COMPANY
                          2444 12125        2437        5869
                                            4937       11469

ARMOUR RESEARCH FOUNDATION OF ILLINOIS INSTITUTE OF
   TECHNOLOGY
  2740  2321                          6156  2697
 11320  2901
        9561

ARMSTRONG CORK COMPANY
  2350 10751  8172  3893  8084  4245  1226         158  4089
  2570 11831        5103              6366        4608  8329
  4750              5933                          6188
  6190
  7180
  7520

ARMSTRONG PATENTS LIMITED, CANADA
                                      9156

ARNOLD EQUIPMENT CORPORATION
                                            7927

ARNOLD, G. WRIGHT
                    6673

ARRO PLASTICS, INC.
                                           10627

ARTHUR ANSLEY MANUFACTURING COMPANY
                          8774

ARUNDALE MANUFACTURING COMPANY
        9721

ARVIN INDUSTRIES, INC.
        5081              8964  8965  8966  8967  8968
                          9694       10886

ASAHI DYESTUFFS MANUFACTURING COMPANY, LIMITED, JAPAN
                                9925

ASAHI ELECTROCHEMICAL INDUSTRIAL COMPANY, LTD., JAPAN
             11062

ASAHI GARASU KABUSHIKI KAISHA (ASAHI GLASS CO., LTD.),
   JAPAN
        4241

ASAHI KASEI KOGYO KABUSHIKI KAISHA, JAPAN
        9701        1183                    2357         619
       11621                                3677

ASBESTOS GUMMIWERKE MARTIN MERKEL K.G., GERMANY
                                            7087

ASEPTIC THERMO INDICATOR COMPANY
  7400                                                  5749

ASHLAND OIL AND REFINING COMPANY
       10061 10062                         11267  1118

ASPRO-NICHOLAS LIMITED, ENGLAND
                                                        8179

ASSOCIATED ELECTRICAL INDUSTRIES LIMITED, ENGLAND
         131  9162  7313          65        6157   298   849
        1141        7813                         11868
        3401

ASSOCIATED LEAD MANUFACTURERS LIMITED, ENGLAND
                                                 10178

ASSOCIATED PULP AND PAPER MILLS LIMITED, AUSTRALIA
                                            7177
```

Figure 7.

carded methods even if they found a way to make the process work effectively. Something new must be added which the patent examiner can not say is obvious to anyone skilled in the art. "Insufficient disclosure" will not be tolerated by the examiners.

Thus, we may see that patents, unlike the periodical literature, are bound by definition to contain new information and data. Further, the data in patents are highly reliable because validity of the patent demands accuracy of information revealed.

REFERENCES

1. Worth Wade, "Legal and Patent Problems in Import-Export Marketing of Chemical Products," *J. Chem. Doc.* Vol. 5, No. 2, (1965), pp. 78-82 (1965).
2. Published by Information for Industry, Inc., 1000 Connecticut Ave. N.W., Washington, D.C., 20036. Reproductions of pages from this Index are by permission of the copyright owner, Information for Industry, Inc.

NODC: AN EXPERIMENT IN RESPONSE TO A NEED FOR SCIENTIFIC INTEGRATION

THOMAS WINTERFELD
NODC (National Oceanographic Data Center)

A national center for oceanographic data was first recommended in 1959 in a report of the working group on Data Recording and Standardization of the Coordinating Committee on Oceanography to the Interagency Committee on Oceanography (ICO). This report emphasized the need for a central repository for oceanographic data collected by various government and private activities. ICO recommended to the Federal Council on Science and Technology that NODC be established and that it be sponsored, financed, and its policies be determined jointly by an Interagency Advisory Board comprised of the following: the Navy, the U.S. Coast and Geodetic Survey, the Weather Bureau, the Bureau of Commercial Fisheries, the Atomic Energy Commission, the National Science Foundation, and, for representation of nongovernment activities, the National Academy of Sciences.

In 1960 the Federal Council gave unanimous approval to these recommendations and the Data Center took on life with the preparation of a charter. The charter envisioned a new concept in the scope of Data Center responsibilities, and it has since profoundly influenced the actual operations of NODC:

> NODC *shall* . . . receive, compile, *process,* and preserve oceanographic data submitted to it . . . be responsible for acquiring by exchange, gifts, or purchase oceanographic data of *scientific value* from domestic and foreign sources. . . . Establish procedures for insuring that the accuracy and general quality of the data incorporated into the Data Center's holdings meet the criteria established by the advisory board and shall undertake *analytical studies* necessary for this purpose. . . . Prepare data summaries and tabulations showing annual and seasonal oceanographic conditions.

This rather broad mandate has proved farsighted and given the Data Center an unusual degree of freedom in the range of its interest. It is also significant to note that the charter defines in some detail what the Data Center shall do but it does not place directly or indirectly any specific obligation on the data originator. This brings us to the significance of the word Experiment in the title of this talk. No one, including U. S. Government activities, is in any way obligated, required, or directed, to submit oceanographic data to the Data Center. The need of the scientist for a central repository of data has long been obvious. Oceanographic data have been collected by numerous and widely dispersed institutions, laboratories, etc. Intensive search, private communications on the national and international level, etc., were required to gather data for specific projects if indeed the existence of data was at all known.

The data originator, however, may perhaps perceive less of an immediate need for a Data Center; in fact the additional effort required to communicate with the Data Center may well be burdensome.

Thus the Data Center, having no legal or regulatory power, must provide inducements to the originator. (Unless of course, the originator, as is often the case, is also a data consumer.) One obvious inducement is to invite broad participation of oceanographic interests in the management of NODC. NODC is, in fact, managed by an Interagency Advisory Panel composed of representatives from almost the entire spectrum of oceanographic activities. In addition to the activities mentioned previously, the U.S. Coast Guard has recently joined the panel and others may join in the near future.

On the international level NODC has established data exchange arrangements with more than 30 countries and with international organizations such as the International Council for the Exploration of the Sea (ICES). Also on the international level the voluntary submissions of data to NODC has been greatly speeded by offering NODC's processing and coordinating services to international oceanographic expeditions, such as the International Indian Ocean Expedition and the International Cooperative Investigations of the Tropical Atlantic. (For the latter NODC is also publishing the voluminous report.)

Acquisition of data from foreign sources is further facilitated by the existence of World Data Center–A, Oceanography (WDC-A), which, not without design, is physically located at NODC and, in fact, shares some of its staff and facilities. World Data Center–B, Oceanography (WDC-B), is located in Moscow. The World Data Center which is a permanent outgrowth of the International Geophysical Year (IGY) program, offers an additional special advantage: by international agreement oceanographic data obtained under nationally declared programs must be expeditiously sent to the WDC's. Receipt of data by WDC-A is, of course, essentially synonymous with acquisition by NODC and this arrangement has proven especially helpful in obtaining data which fill some important gaps in NODC's holdings.

It now might be appropriate to look at what exactly does NODC acquire, hold, etc. It could, of course, be simply assumed that data from any scientific discipline collected in, on, above, or below the ocean are oceanographic data. NODC's charter holds NODC responsible for: chemical, physical, biological, geological, and related information pertaining to the sea. Being only three years old and limited in staff and facilities, NODC has not yet been able to be totally responsive to this broad mandate and has concentrated its energies mainly on that part of the data spectrum which is most clearly particular to oceanography. In brief these are: The classic oceanographic station (serial depth or Nansen cast) data. The usual oceanographic station consists of temperatures and salinity measurements obtained at a number of discrete depth levels, collected by means of sample bottles and thermometers lowered on a wire at a specific place and time, generally from a ship. In addition a number of chemical parameters, such as oxygen, phosphate, nitrates, etc., may be determined for all or some of these levels. Surface conditions at the time of the station, such as weather, sea state, etc., are also generally given. At this time NODC holds about 280,000 oceanographic stations, stored on more than 5 million punch cards, representing more than 9 million individual measurements at various depth levels. The station data constitute by far the largest individual such file in the world and are indexed and archived by the original cruise or expedition on which they were collected and geographically by one degree square of latitude and longitude.

Another major file which is receiving prime emphasis is the Bathythermograph Data (profiles of temperature against depth) file of which more than one million are now available. Unlike the station data which are received in reduced or partially processed form, the bulk of the BT's arrive in raw data form (fragile glass slides, log sheets, and calibration references) and require laborious processing to convert them from a scratch on coated glass to an analogue record of temperature against depth identified in place and time. These data flow in at an accelerating rate of more than 6,000 each month and the required processing is straining the Data Center facilities.

In the biological and geological realm the effort has so far been confined to developing-reporting and punch-card formats in close cooperation with interested scientists and institutions. Few actual data have been acquired so far. Large volumes of surface current data are now stored in various forms such as ledgers, listings, punch cards, summaries, etc., and as an enormous backlog of unprocessed ship reports. An attack on this file is planned for the near future. Sea-surface data collected in conjunction with meteorological observations such as temperature, waves, and marine meteorological data are stored at the National Weather Records Center at Asheville, North Carolina. There is no intention to duplicate these holdings, which amount to tens of millions of observations, at NODC. Instead, study is under way of communication systems which will allow rapid access to specific items of these files as needed. The growing awareness of the importance of the air-sea interface processes will undoubtedly require reevaluating the organization of various oceanic data files and lead to the creation of summarized files applicable to both the atmosphere and the ocean.

A variety of other data such as geophysical data, bottom photographs, recordings of animal noises, deep-current measurements and drift bottle records, bird sightings, optical density, etc., not to mention the endless reels of fathograms collected over the decades, if not acquired actually by the Data Center, must at least be indexed for ready access.

Thus the Data Center hopes to integrate the many disciplines which relate to oceanography by either holding the data or being aware of its existence and location. It should, for example, be able to answer correlative questions such as: "Were phosphate data collected at an oceanographic station with a certain time and distance of, say a plankton tow?" etc., and furnish all applicable data.

I would now like to consider in some detail what is perhaps one of the most significant aspects of NODC's operation—namely, its attempt to integrate the data-producing with the data-consuming or analytical activities. Rather than act merely as a repository of data submitted from the field the Data Center enriches the data, so to speak, by routine processing and by quality control. From the early stages of planning of the Data Center and drawing on the experience with oceanographic data processing at the U. S. Navy Hydrographic Office prior to NODC, it was established that the burden of quality control should not be primarily left to the data consumer. The ever-increasing volume of data make it virtually impossible for the average data consumer to cope with the generally encountered quality control problems.

I would like to illustrate the extent and nature of quality control the Data Center exercises by using oceanographic station data processing as an example. In this case the first step consists of checking the incoming data for uniformity of units, observational and data reduction methods used, etc. Oceanographic station data must undergo elaborate and complex reduction routines before "readings" become "data"; many institutions develop their own data-reducing and reporting methods. If necessary the data are recoded by NODC onto standard forms, nonstandard units are converted to standard units, and additional adjustments are made to insure that the fields to be key-punched will fit the standard field definition.

The data are next key-punched, and incidentally, veripunched, lineproofed, in addition to being indexed, etc. At this point computational processing begins. Based on the observed values certain additional parameters such as sea water density, sound velocity, etc., are computed for all stations. In addition the data are interpolated for a number of standard depth levels and parameters useful to dynamic oceanography are computed. This routine processing has more than doubled the total number of numeric entries and punch cards and added considerably to the cost of data processing. This processing is necessary to produce the kind of data input that is needed for the commonly performed data analyses in physical and dynamical oceanography. The computed parameters are now available, either by cruise or geographically, as a by-product at no additional cost to the consumer; the cost of the data being merely the nominal charge for paper and listing machine time. NODC is, of course, prepared on request, to perform any other computations, but in this case charges for programming and computer costs.

As mentioned above, the current routinely performed computations have been the ones most commonly desired by analysts in the past. As newer analytical requirements develop, NODC will, based partly on review of the nature of requests and on comments received from the oceanographic community, add (or substitute) to its routine computations. For example, while in the past there has been interest primarily in interpolations for standard depth horizons (for study of the environment at particular depths) a demand for interpolations at specific levels of density (in order to study the environment at standard density levels) is becoming more common. In response, NODC is developing a program for standard density interpolation. An experimental interpolation for 70 standard density levels has just been completed on a geographic basis for all station data in the Indian and western Pacific Oceans. Eventually, however, as the magnitude of the file continues to increase, routine updating of the entire file for additional computational elements may become prohibitive.

The major, and we feel the most important, quality-control effort by the Data Center is directed to the scientific plausibility of the data. A data assemblage in a specific area generally consists of data observed (and reduced) by a number of institutions over long periods of time. The evaluation applied to the data by the originators can vary considerably, depending on the observer, institute, etc. Residual errors remain or are introduced in publication, even in the best of data. While the over-all error rate for oceanographic data is low, certain conditions make the tolerance for error very low indeed, considering the complexity and sparseness of data. The 270,000 stations, fully processed by NODC, when distributed over the world's oceans, still leaves many a five-degree square with less than ten stations, and, with a seasonal breakdown or at greater depths, the coverage becomes sparser. In other words, a faulty value may make up a significant percentage of data available at a particular area, and depth level, and normal statistical approaches to identify error are often not feasible. Further, a single error at a shallow level may introduce error in the computation at all succeeding levels.

The plausibility of oceanographic data can, however, generally be evaluated within broad limits by inspecting its "fit" into the environment. For this the Data Center is in a uniquely favorable position, since it conveniently has on hand all data for the generation of environmental quality-control models. In the case of station data, the chief criteria used for quality control are the "fit" of the data into certain well-established relationships which define the water masses of the ocean, the stability of the water column, and rate of change of parameter against depth. Up to the present time this task has been performed by the simple but very tedious method of monitoring all computed data on a production basis for plausibility using experienced professional oceanographers. The plausibility of the data is determined within liberal limits predicated on the requirements of normal regional analysis. It must be strongly emphasized, to allay misgivings on the part of the scientist objecting to the preanalysis (or cooking) of data, that no data are ever suppressed or altered; they are retained, provided with a special indicator, and released along with accompanying data and can therefore be salvaged at any time. For obvious reasons they are, however, by-passed in the interpolation and computation steps.

There are some definite shortcomings to this "personalized" approach to quality control. Besides requiring the services of highly trained personnel on a continuous production basis, it is impossible to avoid a certain amount of subjectivity in evaluating data since no two oceanographers will draw upon quite the same background of knowledge and training. Also, the present system must, for reasons of economy, work on a yes-no basis; the data are either valid or doubtful with no shades of gray permitted.

To put its quality control on a more modern footing, NODC is now developing automated, or at any rate, semiautomated control methods. When the plans become operational the incoming data will be compared by the computer against certain models and criteria and the deviation of the data from the model will become part of the permanent record. The definition of what is "doubtful" will then chiefly depend on the precision requirements of specific analyses (in fact, it will be possible to select by computer sets of data within specified limits of deviation). It is anticipated that the initial control models will be only first assumptions and the system will be designed to be self-improving; as more and more data and populations of deviation become available the models will be adjusted to correct for any bias.

A recent quality control test using a set of actual water mass models was performed in connection with the Equatorial Atlantic Expedition. The results were very encouraging. Though the models were based on sparse coverage of historic data, the data obtained by most of the ships of the expedition fitted within very close tolerances and showed little bias. Only one ship, operated by a group with limited experience in oceanography, stood out by a drastically larger dispersion of data.

It may also be possible to utilize the control models as a sort of intercalibration device. By taking advantage of modern communication facilities ships could radio in their data and be advised of any quality problem before amassing further faulty and very costly data.

It goes without saying that the development of quality control criteria methods and the formulation of environmental models requires analysis. An analysis group has been in operation from the beginning of the Data Center although its energies have at times been diverted by the surprisingly large number of requests not for data but for analyzed products. Another task of the analysis group is to issue reports of the quality problems of the archived data files. For example, using the information in the file of thousands of processing folders of individual Bathythermograph (BT) records, a recent study was conducted on the problem of the accuracy of BT temperature data. This study indicates that the method used to compensate for the bias of a BT instrument may well add a large bias of its own.

Another link between the data consumer and the data observer is furnished by NODC through the design of standard reporting formats; i.e., coding forms, manuals, and punch-card formats. The formats are submitted for comment to the oceanographic community prior to their adoption. In this manner the Data Center also serves as a focal point for other divergent views on specific items. It is hoped the final format will reflect the need for specific kinds of data and the optimum manner of reporting. Admittedly it is not possible to take in all points of view, considering the basic limitations of usable standard forms, but special arrangements for special requirements are always possible on a project basis. To encourage wide use of the formats they are available without charge with multilingual explanatory wrappers and imprinted specially for expedition use if desired.

When the processing has been completed and data are ready to be archived, another problem, which can be considered a form of quality control, arises for a Data Center which wishes to be consumer-oriented: In what manner shall the data be stored? Besides the consideration of format such as listings, punch cards, or magnetic tape, what should be the sorting arrangement of the data files to minimize cost to the consumer? A geographic arrangement would ordinarily be the most immediate choice being the obvious input to environmental studies, but in oceanography many requests, especially from the data originator, must be anticipated in terms of expeditions or cruises. For station data this dilemma has been solved by duplicating the cruise file geographically (and incidentally doubling the file volume). The cruise file is, of course, always somewhat more up to date than the geographically sorted file which is updated periodically. The dual file poses additional problems in respect to corrections submitted by the originator, often many years after receipt of data.

The one million Bathythermograph observations are now filed geographically in analogue format on 3 $\times$ 5 cards. Here is an example of a data system which is not consumer oriented; the output of the BT is analogue and it is currently the only data yielding a continuous record of temperature against depth. However, studies of the distribution of temperatures or temperature gradients cannot be easily undertaken with analogue cards as input. (For example, more than 80,000 BT's are available for the Grand Banks.) To convert the BT's into truly useful data, they must obviously be digitized. NODC has begun an intensive effort to convert this file into a digital product suitable for computer analysis. Prior to digitization, NODC's quality control group conducted studies to determine the optimum number of points which must be digitized to retain the information implied by the analogue trace, without introducing prohibitive cost. The BT record may perhaps be taken as the most striking example of NODC's endeavor to integrate the data producer with the needs of the data consumer. From an original record consisting of scratched uncalibrated glass slides, log sheets (and a file of more than 16,000 individual calibration grids, which requires continual updating) the data are processed into a digital file of punch cards and magnetic tape, in a uniform set of units, geographically sorted and are now suitable as data input for statistical analysis by computer.

In closing I would like to return briefly to a segment of the NODC charter which directs the Data Center to prepare data summaries showing annual and seasonal conditions. In its three years of existence, only a very modest start has been made in this direction. Of course, some of the analyses performed for quality-control purposes, furnish by-products suitable for publication. An atlas of water masses (as defined by the temperature-salinity function) is planned for the near future. Some preliminary atlas work is also under way for the Indian Ocean Expedition. But all indications are that the efforts in this direction must be intensified. The volume of data is large and growing rapidly; in many areas there already exist more data than an analyst or even a team of analysts can reasonably digest. Newer more sophisticated instrumentation will increase the rate of inflow exponentially.

The preparation and design of data summaries which condense the original files into meaningful information, keeping to a minimum the distortion inherent in summary products, are two of the immediate challenges for the Data Center.

AVAILABILITY AND CREATIVE USE OF TOPOGRAPHIC DATA

MORRIS M. THOMPSON
U. S. Geological Survey

It is my privilege to represent an organization that has been in the information business for eighty-five years. The U.S. Geological Survey was established by Congress in 1879 for the purpose of making a systematic study of the geology and natural resources of the United States.

We know that eighty-five years is a long period in terms of the rate of explosion of scientific data. That's enough time for an organization to develop such manifestations of age as hardening of the arteries of communication, and the perpetuation of horse-and-buggy concepts, unless appropriate measures are taken to maintain its vigor and freshness of outlook. If we are to avoid senility we find that we must continually examine and reexamine the nature of the information we present, the manner of its presentation, and the means of making it available to those who have use for it.

THE NATURE OF TOPOGRAPHIC DATA

Of the many kinds of information disseminated by the Geological Survey, I will discuss only one: topographic data. It should be mentioned in passing, however, that several other papers like this could be prepared on the geologic, hydrologic, conservation, and other data available from the Geological Survey.

Topography may be defined as the configuration of a given portion of the earth's surface, including its relief and the position of its natural and manmade features. It embraces the hills, the valleys, the lakes, the rivers, the seacoasts, the woods, swamps, prairies, railroads, highways, streets, trails, houses, schools, churches, factories, boundaries. . . . The list goes on and on, approaching a complete inventory of everything that is there. Topography is translated into topographic data when we have qualitative and quantitative information regarding specific topographic features.

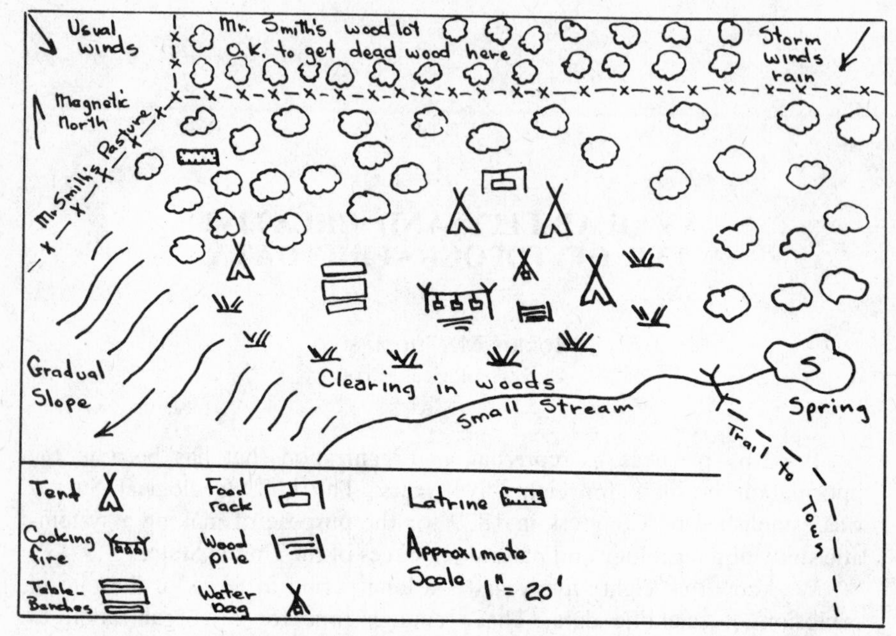

Figure 1. This Boy Scout sketch has the essential attributes of a topographic map. (*Handbook for Boys,* Boy Scouts of America)

Topographic data differ from other kinds of data in that the information is usually presented in continuous rather than discrete form. This continuous presentation of a number of topographic facts is called a topographic map. In Fig. 1 we see a topographic map taken from the *Boy Scout Handbook*. It is crude and not very accurate, but it still has the attributes of a topographic map, giving a pretty good picture of the lay of the land at the camp site. Some measurements or estimates of distance had to be made to draw the map, and it has a scale and a north arrow as well as information on relief, hydrology, culture, woodland, and natural resources; we have here, then, a useful presentation of qualitative and quantitative topographic data, approximate though it may be.

At the other extreme, we now look at Fig. 2 which shows a portion of a Geological Survey topographic map, in this case the White Plains, N.Y. 7½-minute quadrangle (that is, 7½ minutes of latitude by 7½ minutes of longitude) published at a scale of 1:24,000. This map is an example of the kind of topographic data we are going to discuss. It contains a virtually endless amount of information. By reference to the grid and the graticule (marked on the border of the map, but not shown in the figure) we can find the position on the earth's surface of any point on the map, accurate within 40 feet, in terms of State grid coordinates or latitude and longitude.

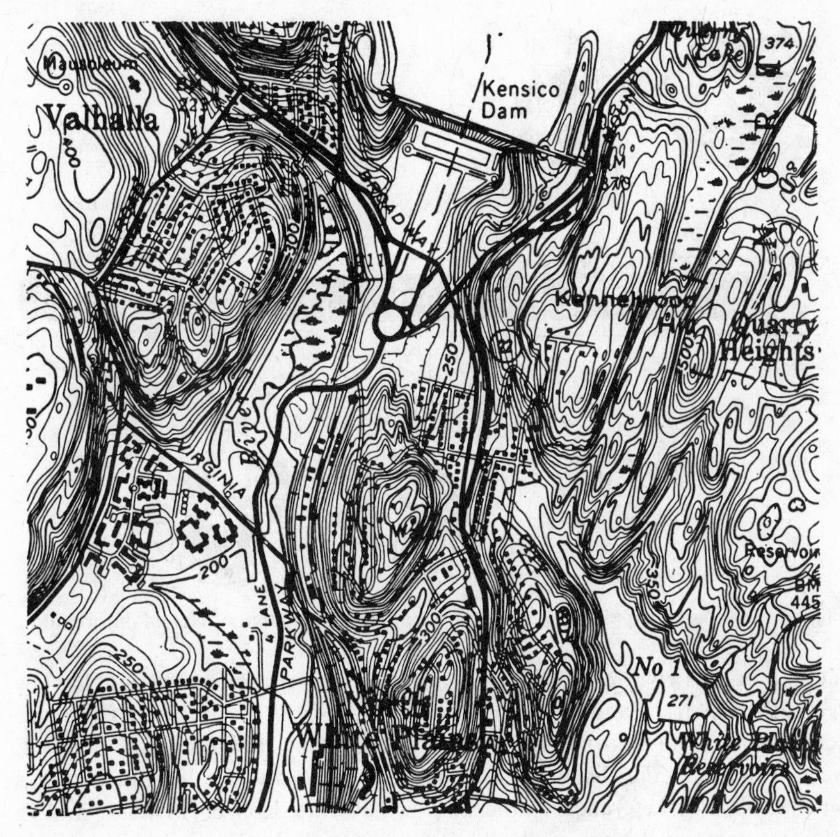

Figure 2. Portion of a modern topographic map, the White Plains, N. W., 7½-minute quadrangle. Scale, 1:24,000.

By reference to the contours we can find the elevation above sea level of any point on the map, accurate in this case within 5 feet. Consider what this means in terms of every point in the United States, when the mapping job is finished: How many measurements have to be made to obtain these facts? How many bits of information are presented? We can't answer these questions, because modern mapmaking techniques (Fig. 3) are actually based more on continuous plotting than on discrete measurements, so that the bits of information presented are, in effect, infinite in number.

To take a closer look at the kind of information we can obtain from a topographic map, consider Fig. 4 which is a portion of the Menan Buttes, Idaho, quadrangle. First, we can see the shapes of features: the typical conical form of the two extinct volcanoes, with the depression contours indicating the craters; the distorted surface of the old lava bed;

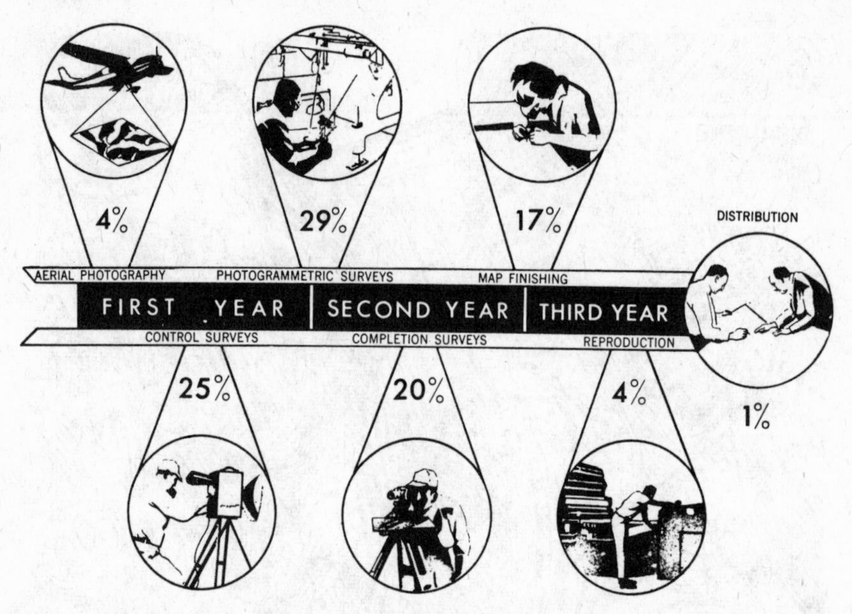

Figure 3. Modern mapping entails the presentation of countless bits of information.

the curvaceous river course and the oxbow relics of its former course. The geologist can trace much of the geological history of the area from this geomorphological information without making any measurements. Second, we can measure the distance accurately between any two identified points on the map, by reference to the map scale printed on every map; and in addition, we can determine the position north of the Equator and west of Greenwich for each point. Third, using the contours, we can measure differences in height between any two points on the map–for example, how deep is the north crater and how high is it above sea level? Fourth, we have an inventory of the works of man: railways, roads, towns, buildings, boundaries . . . and so on. Fifth, we have the names of places and physical features. Sixth, we have a delineation of woodland areas (if there are any).

The next four exhibits (not shown here) represent topographic maps illustrating the great variety of the features and other information shown on maps of different parts of the country. The Cumberland, Md., map exemplifies the spectacular water gaps of the Appalachian Region. The Lake Wales, Fla., map represents a flat, intensively cultivated agricultural area. The New Haven, Conn., quadrangle illustrates the wealth of hydrographic information available on maps of coastal areas, as well as the intricacies of an urban complex. The Washington West, D.C., map is

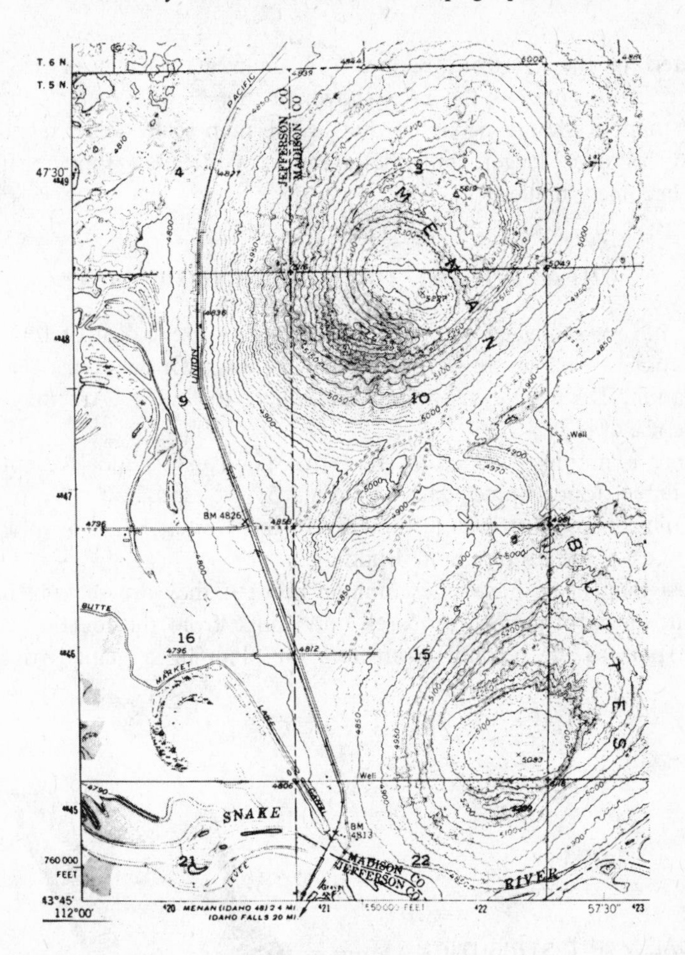

Figure 4. Portion of Menan Buttes, Idaho, topographic map, showing volcanic cinder cones. Maps like this offer a wealth of information to the geologist.

presented to show that we can sit here in this room and from a topographic map determine our latitude and longitude, our elevation above sea level and above the Potomac River, the distance to the White House, and the shortest walking route to the waterfront.

The 7½-minute series of maps we have just looked at represents one of several in the National Topographic Map Series, of which I would like to mention two others. The next exhibit (not shown here) is a 15-minute map of the Frostburg, Md., quadrangle, showing in its northeast quarter the same area we saw in the Cumberland, Md., quadrangle; this map has a scale of 1:62,500, or 1 inch = 1 mile, nearly. Still another map series is illustrated in the Hartford, Conn.-N.Y. map at a scale of 1:250,000; included in this map is the area shown on the New Haven, Conn., 7½-minute map. It should be noted that as the map scale decreases, the area covered becomes larger, but the amount of detailed topographic data shown becomes smaller.

CREATIVE USE OF TOPOGRAPHIC MAPS

We have established the fact that there is a great deal of topographic information available. It is logical to ask next: Of what use is all this information? Do people know how and where to find it? Are they making creative use of it?

There is ample evidence to show that good use is indeed being made of available topographic data. In Fig. 5, we see how the 6 million topographic maps distributed annually in the United States would look if stacked beside the Empire State Building.

Most map users have one common motive: they are seeking information; but the information they seek may range from the location of likely fishing spots to the terrain parameters for planning a giant hydroelectric

ANNUAL MAP DISTRIBUTION

....would make a stack higher than the Empire State Building, and the number is growing steadily year by year.

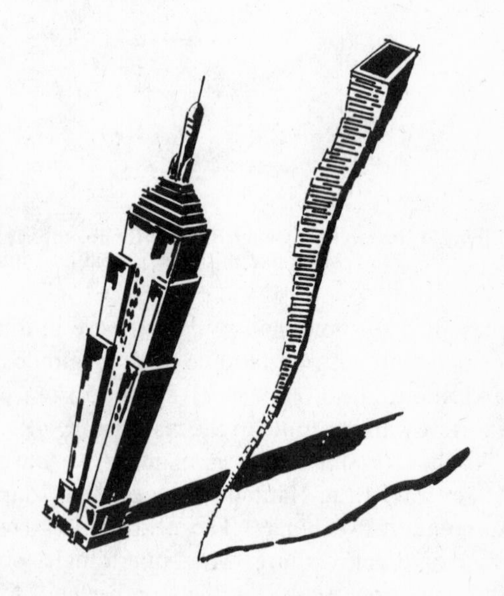

Figure 5. Annual distribution of topographic maps.

plant. It would be impossible to categorize all the users of topographic maps, but we can at least list some of the more prominent map users whose interest is evidenced by official requests to the Geological Survey for topographic mapping of the area of their interest:

Federal Agencies

Agricultural Research Service
Agricultural Stabilization and Conservation Service
Forest Service
Soil Conservation Service
Corps of Engineers
Bureau of the Census
Bureau of Public Roads
Coast and Geodetic Survey
Weather Bureau
Health, Education and Welfare
Bureau of Indian Affairs
Bureau of Land Management
Bureau of Mines
Bureau of Outdoor Recreation
Bureau of Reclamation
Fish and Wildlife Service
National Park Service
Atomic Energy Commission
Federal Aviation Agency
Tennessee Valley Authority
National Aeronautics and Space Administration

State Agencies

- Departments of
  - Conservation
  - Engineering
  - Highways
  - Internal Affairs
  - Mines
  - Natural Resources
  - Public Works
  - Registration and Education
  - Water Resources
- Geological Survey
- Public Utilities Commissions

Topographic maps are used creatively on many fronts by knowledgeable groups such as these who know that the topographic data already available can save them prodigious amounts of time, effort, and money that would otherwise be required for surveys, searches, and data compilations. Some of these uses are given in Fig. 6.

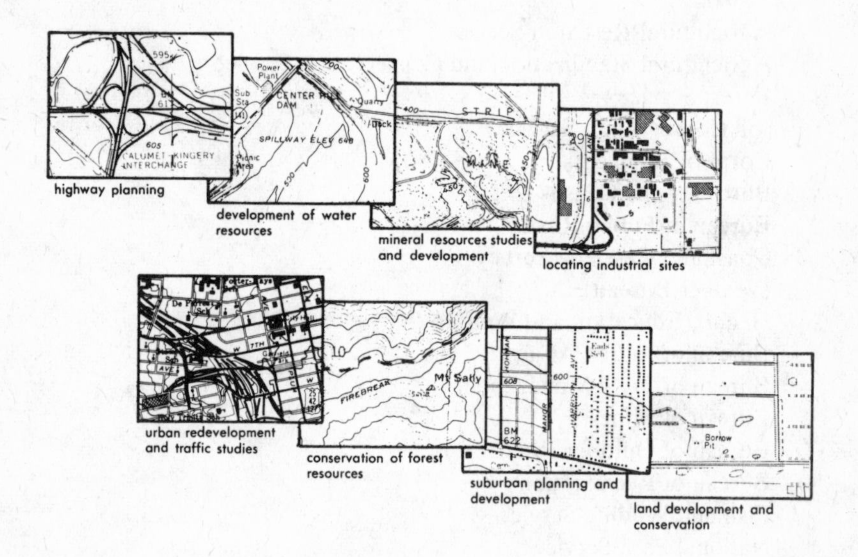

Figure 6. Some uses of topographic maps.

The next three illustrations portray specific scientific and engineering applications of topographic data. Fig. 7 relates to a scientific problem in locating a giant radio telescope. In order to eliminate radio interference from extraneous sources, it was required that this telescope be located in a bowl-shaped depression having terrain parameters lying within a fixed range of dimension and form. The ideal area shown in the figure was found by searching topographic maps, an effort that was minor in cost compared to the cost of the field exploration that would have been required had there been no maps.

Fig. 8 shows a highway location planned for maximum efficiency and economy. Modern electronic computers utilizing detailed topographic data have greatly simplified and speeded up the process of route selection and highway design.

In Fig. 9 the layout of Dulles International Airport on a topographic map illustrates how information concerning the exact nature of the terrain was utilized in this great engineering project.

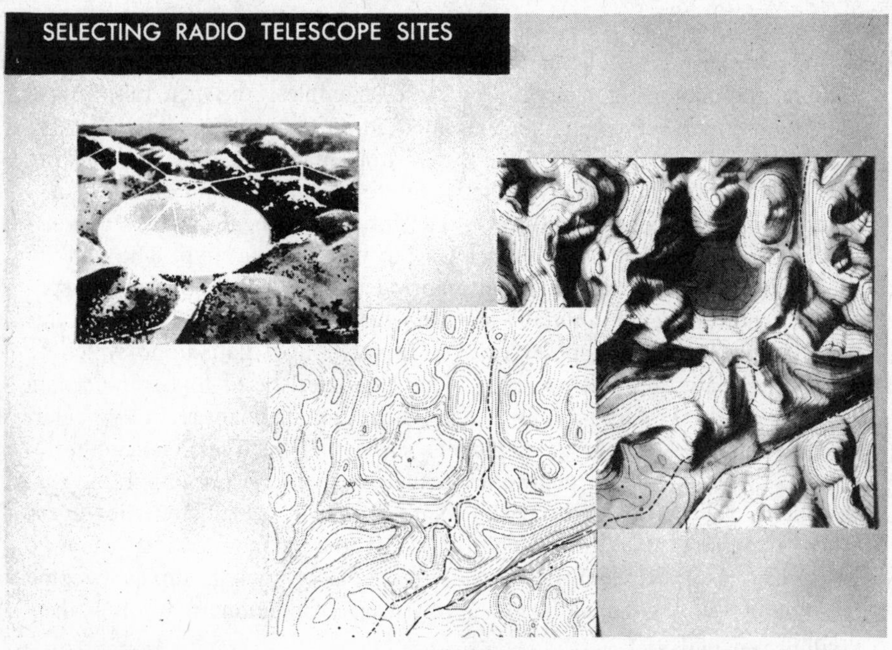

Figure 7. Selecting radio telescope sites is facilitated by use of topographic maps.

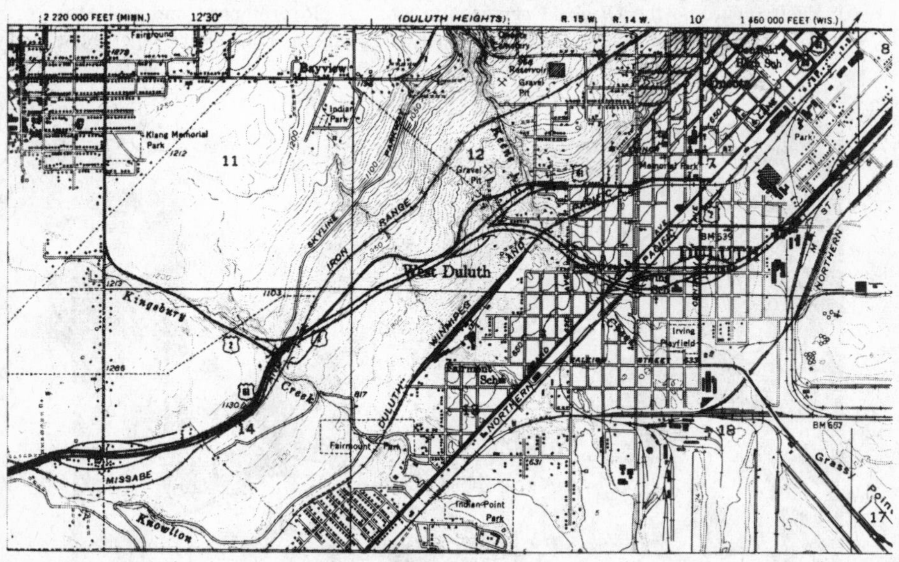

Figure 8. Topographic quadrangle maps play a vital part in planning highway routes.

In addition to the direct and immediate use of available topographic data in the manner illustrated by these examples, the general-purpose topographic map serves another extremely important purpose as a base for other data. The geologist can use the existing map as a base for showing strikes and dips, lithologic contacts, outcrops, unconformities and many other items of geologic significance. The forester delineates stands of various kinds and conditions of timber on the topographic map. The wildlife specialist plots on the topographic map the natural haunts of various species of wildfowl, game animals, fish, and birds and beasts of prey. In this way, the topographic map serves as a foundation of data upon which to build other data, in endless variety. This characteristic of topographic data was recognized as far back as 1885, when Captain George M. Wheeler, leader of one of the four great pioneer surveys of the West, said of topographic surveys: "The topographic is the indispensable all-important survey, being general and not special in its character, which underlies every other, including also the graphic basis of the economic and scientific examinations of the country. . . . The results of such a survey become the mother source whence all other physical examinations may draw their graphic sustenance."*

* Facts regarding the Origin, Organization, etc., of Government Land and Marine Surveys of the United States, 1885. Pamphlet. Washington, D.C. War Department.

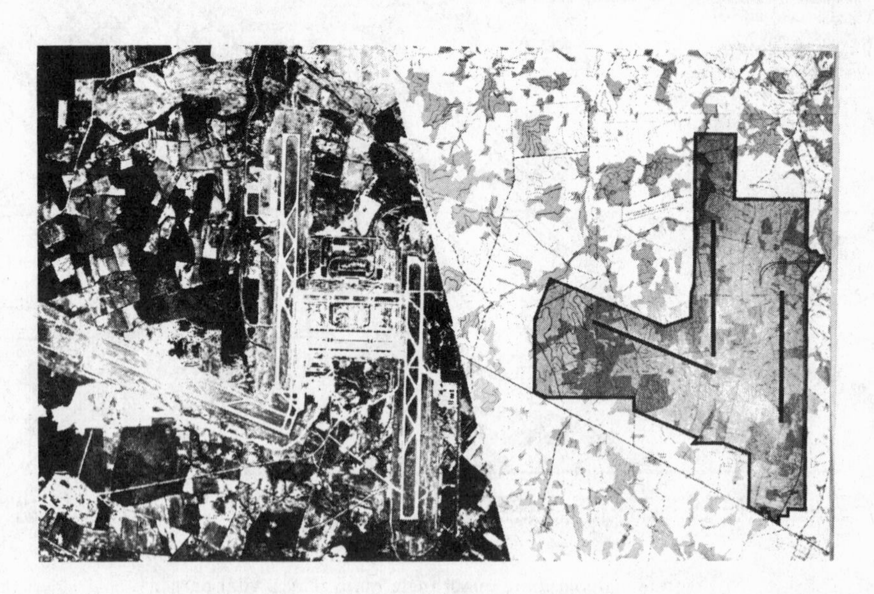

Figure 9. Topographic maps are used to select airport sites.

AVAILABILITY OF TOPOGRAPHIC DATA

All of this basic topographic data would not be of much help if the users did not know where to find it. Fortunately, the United States has one central clearing house for such data. The Map Information Office, a national office located within the Geological Survey, was established in 1919 for disseminating, surveying and mapping information to other agencies at all levels of Government and to the general public as well. In addition to providing information regarding topographic maps produced by any government agency, the Map Information Office annually handles thousands of requests for data dealing with aerial photographs (a basic source of topographic data) and geodetic control surveys.

Figure 10. Portion of a topographic map index for the State of New York.

As in most other procedures for information retrieval, the key to the location of needed topographic data is an index, exemplified by Fig. 10, part of an index for the State of New York. There is one important difference: a topographic index is not a list of code words or phrases, but a map. There is also an important similarity between a modern conventional index and a topographic index: the topographic index is a system of coordinate indexing, except that in this case the coordinates are not words, but numbers, namely latitude and longitude. The topographic index is coded so that for each quadrangle we can determine the name of the quadrangle, its size (7½ or 15 minutes), where it is located, whether a map of the quadrangle has been published, and the date of publication.

Each year, the Map Information Office produces the widely distributed index map entitled *Status of Topographic Mapping in the United States,* shown in part in Fig. 11. This status map shows by colors and patterns the areas covered by existing topographic maps produced by agencies of the Federal government, and the scales of the maps. Also, for each map scale, the status map indicates (but not in the example printed here) in which of four grades of quality each map is classified, beginning with the highest grade, which includes the newer up-to-date maps produced from standard-accuracy surveys, and ending with the lowest grade of old, obsolete, reconnaissance-type maps. In addition, the status map shows where new topographic surveys are in progress, as well as those areas where no topographic quadrangle maps of the National series are yet available.

LIMITS ON DATA AVAILABILITY

The availability of topographic data is limited by three factors:

1. Some parts of the country have never been mapped by 7½-minute or 15-minute standards.
2. Topographic data rapidly becomes obsolete in areas of growth and change.
3. The scale and accuracy of the available maps are not adequate for some purposes.

As of now, about 70 percent of the country is covered by 7½-minute or 15-minute maps, as shown in Fig. 11, and complete coverage is expected by 1976. This completion date, however, is small comfort to the map user who needs the information now. Nevertheless we are making good progress, as demonstrated by comparing Fig. 11 with Fig. 12 which shows the status of topographic mapping in the United States in 1947, about 27 percent complete by modern standards.

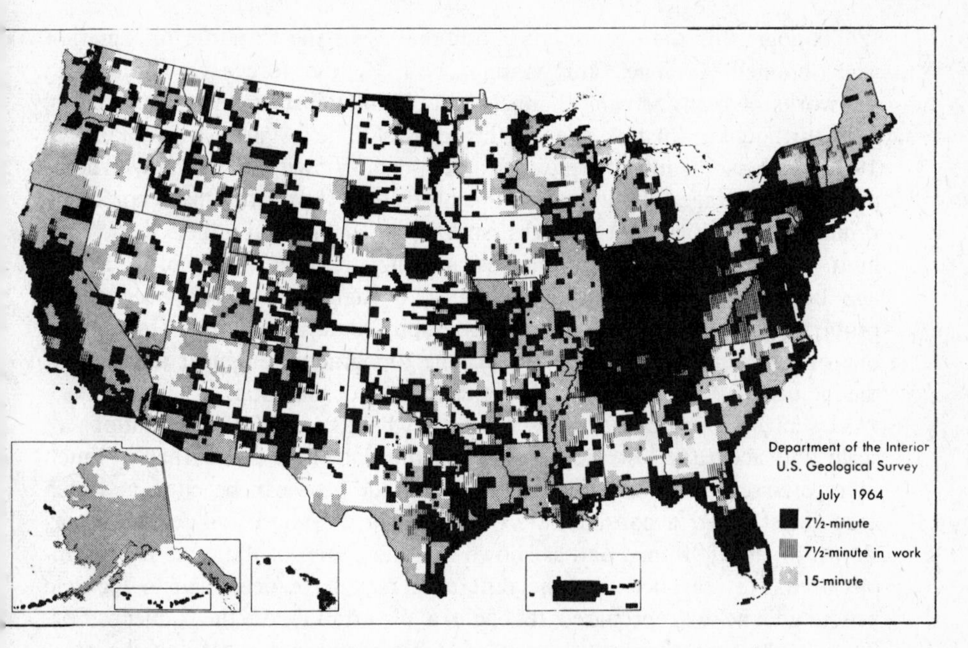

Figure 11. Status of topographic mapping in the United States, 1964.

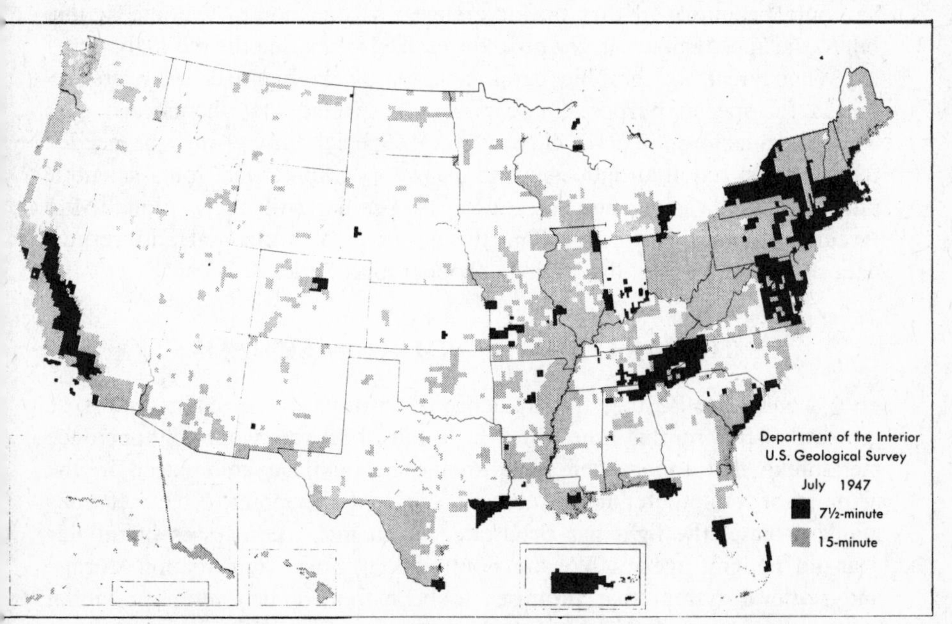

Figure 12. Status of topographic mapping in the United States, 1947.

Topographic data represent conditions as of the time the information was obtained. Changes are wrought both by the forces of nature and the works of man. Stream channels shift, mountainsides slide into valleys, and earthquakes distort the earth's crust. (The Alaska earthquake of 1964 made some of the physiographic data shown on the newly completed Anchorage quadrangle map obsolete before the map could be printed.) As cities and suburbs spread, as dams and other works are built, the face of the earth changes and the up-to-date map of a decade ago becomes obsolete and inadequate for many of today's needs. The problem of continual revision of topographic data as conditions change is one of the toughest challenges facing the topographic engineer and one of the factors that can severely limit the usefulness of the data.

Users of topographic maps need also be aware of the limitations of scale and accuracy lest they try to use the data in a sense that is much more precise than is inherent in the map. One case can be cited in which a geologist noted a considerable difference in elevation and form data as shown on an 1890 map and as shown on a new map of the same mountainous area. He reasoned that the difference may have been due to tectonic action and he was prepared to begin a dissertation on the subject. Fortunately, he was sufficiently knowledgeable to inquire regarding the relative accuracy of the two maps; enough information was available so that he could be informed that the difference was due not to tectonic action, but to the approximate survey procedures used in making the old map.

When great topographic detail and extremely high accuracy are required for special purposes, it cannot be expected that the needed data will be available on general-purpose maps. Special surveys may be needed to obtain the required data. Anyone using topographic data for a scientific purpose should, as a matter of course, be familiar with the National Map Accuracy Standards which define the accuracy of horizontal and vertical data shown on maps of the National Topographic Series.

TOPOGRAPHIC INFORMATION SYSTEMS

I would surmise that this audience of information specialists must be growing restive by this time, for I have talked all this while without once mentioning that topographic data should be digitized and placed in the memory of a computer for instant retrieval. At this point, I can set your minds at ease; the light has penetrated, even into the recesses of an 85-year-old Federal agency. We are now working on an information storage and retrieval system that promises to be extremely helpful in providing quick access to selected items of topographic data (Fig. 13).

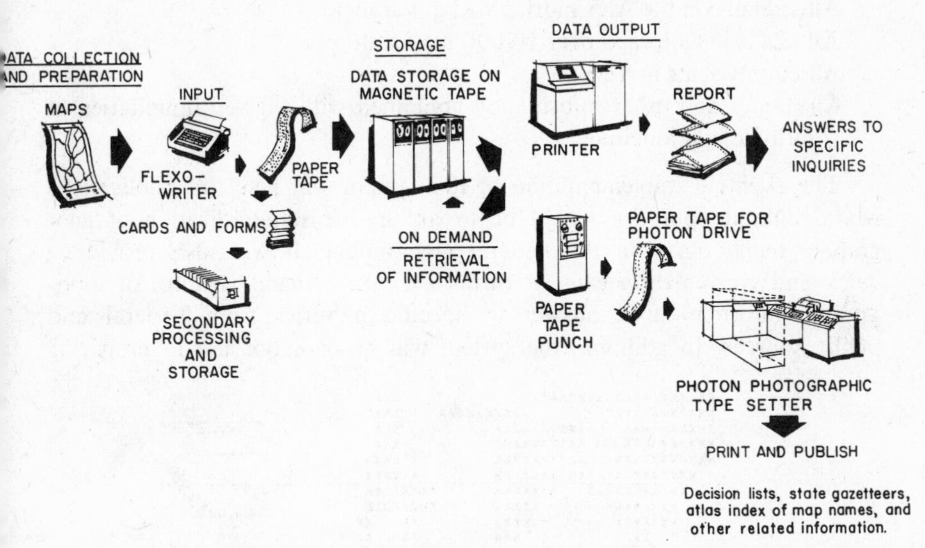

Figure 13. Storage and retrieval of topographic data.

Designed for use primarily in the processing and publication of geographic names, the system will provide an information store consisting of names of places and features and the following data for each name:

Designation or description
Area location (political/administrative subdivision)
Population where applicable
Elevations where applicable
Latitude and longitude
Quadrangle identification
Variant names

Other items pertaining to description, location, or history of each name.

Input data for the computer will consist of punched paper tapes, converted and stored on magnetic tape. Retrieval according to the user's needs can be achieved through a high-speed printer or in paper-tape form to drive a photographic typesetting machine called the Photon.

For the orderly filing of data and easy access to the store, a coded hierarchical classification system is being developed analagous to a classification schedule used for filing and retrieving maps or other documents. By consulting the classification code, the user will be able to retrieve information in groupings or categories such as:

All stored names for the State of California in alphabetical order

All streams on the Alexandria, Va., quadrangle
All peaks in Colorado over 10,000 feet in altitude
All county seats in Texas
All names and other information contained within given boundaries of latitude and longitude.

The eventual implementation of this system will result in publications whose ultimate purpose would be to aid in the standardization of geographic name usage in the Federal government. It will also provide a quick and convenient means of furnishing "on demand" listings of topographic information in answer to specific inquiries from Federal and public sources. In addition, the system will be of major use in preparing

```
XXXXXXXXXXXXXXXXXXXX          XXX
XXXXXXXXXXX       XXXXXXXXX   XXX
XXXXXXXXXX   XXXXXXXXXX       XXX
XXXXXXXXXX   XXXXXXXXXX       XXX
XXXXXXXXXXX  XXXXXXXXXX     XXXXXX
  XXXXXXXXXX XXXXXXXXXX     XXXXXX            30
   XXXXXXXXXXX  XXXXXXX   XXXXXXXX
    XXXXXXXX      XXXXX   XXXXXXXX
    XXXXXXX       XXXXX     XX   XX
       XX          XXXX     XX   XX
                    XXXXXXX       XX
                     XXXXXX       XX
                      XXXXXXX      XX
                      X XXXXX      XX         29
                         XXXX       XX
                         XXXX   X   XXX
                         XXXXXX   XX XXXX
                         XXXXXX   XXXXXXXXX
                         XXXXXXXXXXXXXXXXXX
                         XXXXXXXXXXXXXXXXXX
                        XXXXXXXXXXXXXXXXXXX
                        XXXXXXXXXXXXXXXXXXX   28
                        XXXXXXXXXXXXXXXXXXXX
                        XXXXXXXXXXXXXXXXXXXX
                         XXXXXXXXXXXXXXXXXXXX
                        XXXXXXXXXXXXXXXXXXXXX
                         XXXXXXXXXXXXXXXXXXXX
                          XXXXXXXXXXXXXXXXXXXX
                          XXXXXXXXXXXXXXXXXXXX
                           XXXXXXXXXXXXX XXXXXX  27
                           XXXXXXXXXX        XX
                            XXXXXXXXX        XX
                            XXXXXXXXX        XX
                             XXXXXXXX        XX
                             XXXXXXXX        XX
                                XXXXX        XX
                                XXXXX        XX
                                XXXXX        XX  26
                                            XX
                                            XX
                                           XXX
                                          XXXX
                                          XXXX
                                          XXXX
                                           XX
                                           X     25


                                XXX
                               XXXX


                                                 24
86      85      84      83      82      81      80      79
```

Figure 14. Portion of *TAG* printout showing locations of completed 7½-minute topographic maps in Florida.

the index and other materials for the forthcoming National Atlas of the United States.

The computer is used in still another way in a system called TAG (Tabulation and Graphic) which provides for the indication of information pertaining to specific topographic quadrangle maps on a rectangular coordinate system representing the United States or parts thereof. Any one of ten possible classes of information can be indicated in a particular quadrangle position in the system. For example, Fig. 14 is part of a printout from a Burroughs 220 computer showing the locations of all completed 7½-minute quadrangle maps in the South Atlantic States. Five strips of these charts mosaicked together are needed to produce a graphical representation of information for the 48 conterminous States. Currently only one class of information is printed out on one sheet of paper; however, we are now in the process of writing the program for printing out variable information on a single pass.

We are only beginning to exploit the possibilities of computer-based information-retrieval systems in the utilization of topographic data. On the other hand, computers now play an important role in the preparation of this data—in the mapmaking operation itself. It is logical to predict that the computer experience obtained in the production of topographic data will spill over more and more into the retrieval of the same data.

CONCLUSION

Topographic information is an important tool of science and society. It is abundantly available in many areas, to those who know how to obtain and use it. It has some limitation in that there are still some areas where topographic data is lacking or out-of-date; also, available topographic data may not be as precise as they need to be for certain specialized purposes.

Modern information-retrieval principles, using computer storage, can be applied profitably to topographic data in many instances; but the topographic map retains the advantage of continuous, graphical presentation of data. There is a place and a need for both the continuous picture and the quick retrieval of discrete items of information. We can expect an increasing use of topographic data in both forms.

REFERENCES

1. J. O. Kilmartin, "The Function of a National Map Information Office," paper presented at the IX Consultation on Cartography, PAIGH, Buenos Aires, Argentina, 1961. (Obtainable from U.S. Geological Survey.)

2. W .B. Overstreet and R. B. Wong, "Automated System for Planning and Controlling a Mapping Program," paper presented at 24th Annual Meeting of the American Congress on Surveying and Mapping, March 1964. (Obtainable from U.S. Geological Survey.)
3. J. A. Roberts, "The Topographic Map in a World of Computer," *The Professional Geographer,* Vol. XIV, No. 6 (November 1962).

DISCUSSION

Question: Would you like to comment on the time scale for developing this computer programming?

Answer: We are only in the early phases right now. But some elements are available. For example, the computer-instructed typesetter does exist. You can instruct it to set place names on a certain scale and in a certain style of type. The beauty of it is instead of having type fonts with many different sizes of type you use only one font for a particular style which you reproduce photographically at any size within a wide range. The machine produces copy from which you can make stick-up lettering which you can apply directly to a map. Our office in Menlo Park, California or Denver, Colorado can send the information in on tape and it goes directly into the system. I can't tell you much about the time scale for programming the retrieval of general topographic information. We are confining our present effort to geographic names information which in itself is a subject that involves the processing of a tremendous amount of data.

Question: Is this an operational project or is it still in the brainstorm stage?

Answer: The whole thing is still in the brainstorm stage. The automatic typesetter is operational, but that doesn't give topographic data in the sense of answering specific questions.

Question: Do you call this machine on the right in the illustration "Photon"?

Answer: That's right, Photon.

Question: How do you tie in the Army maps and smaller tactical maps with your program?

Answer: All the mapping activities of the Federal Government are coordinated through the Bureau of Budget. The Army Map Service has responsibility for certain overseas mapping plus military areas in the United States. The Geological Survey is responsible for domestic topographic mapping. The Coast and Geodetic Survey executes surveys for basic geodetic control and maps coastal areas. We use their geodetic control in our mapping.

Question: Who has the responsibility for the bench marks?

Answer: The first- and second-order bench marks are the Coast and Geodetic Survey responsibility. We expand beyond that into third-order and fourth-order for our map control.

Question: Does the Budget Bureau have technical people who act as a referral center on mapping to avoid duplication?

Answer: Yes, they have an adviser on cartography and they coordinate the activities so that there is no duplication. Some people may think there is duplication because we use similar equipment and have similar working activities. That is, if a man is out in the field surveying with a transit or theodolite, he may be doing primary control for the Coast and Geodetic Survey, or he may be doing map control for the Geological Survey. But the work of the agencies is coordinated.

Question: Do you have plastic relief maps?

Answer: We recently produced one and only one in Antarctica, because we have the responsibility for mapping Antarctica. This is a very unusual one by the way. It's in two layers. The top layer is transparent and shows the snow and ice surface. You lift that up and on another layer is the solid surface under the snow and ice. Only a small number were produced and distribution was restricted to individuals and organizations closely associated with Antarctic research.

Question: Are you expecting to broaden the scope of this plastic relief map activity in the future?

Answer: No. The Army Map Service already does a great deal of this work. We have all we can do to keep up with our primary program and we have continual demands for all sorts of other things.

Question: How many people are in your division of the Geological Survey and what is your budget?

Answer: The Topographic Division has about 2,200 people and our annual budget is on the order of $26 million. It's really a very small budget. I recently took a course in this series on Research Administration and the Defense people here were talking about contracts and they said a contractor is not a major contractor unless the contract is for at least 25 million dollars. Contractors also come to us with proposals and they may have very good schemes for mapping, but if it takes 40 million dollars to work it out, there goes our complete budget for two years. The best we can do is to encourage some agency with more money to sponsor the development.

EPIC—ECONOMIC PROGRESS through INTERNATIONAL COMMUNICATION ©

The United States Government

ALBERT N. ABAJIAN
Research Associate
Center for Technology and Administration
The American University, Washington, D.C.

INTRODUCTION

For several hundred thousand years man existed on earth in a nomadic hunting and fishing environment, his economic development sorely restricted by his personal attributes and sensibilities and by his limited ability to communicate his thoughts and knowledge to his contemporaries and descendants.

About 65 hundred years ago, the dependency of man's economic progress upon his ability to communicate with his fellow-man across the barriers of distance, time, language, and culture was firmly established on the banks of the Tigris and Euphrates Rivers. His flourishing commerce, trade, transportation, and his banking requirements significantly influenced the invention of writing, the beginning of recorded history, and the start of civilization. The development of his separate but interrelated pursuits and the interactions between them down through the centuries to the present day have affected the course of history and helped enrich man's life on earth. In turn, man's economic development has been continuingly conditioned by his ability to acquire the knowledge of his predecessors, to communicate his thoughts and knowledge to his contemporaries, and to store his knowledge for use by his successors.

Man's continuing economic progress and the efficient conduct of his affairs is now threatened by the magnitude and complexity of his communication and information requirements. The accelerating rate of change that man has brought about by the scientific and technological revolution has ushered in an era of unprecedented communication problems. I would like to review briefly this morning that aspect of international communication in the Government which directly affects the achievement of United States economic goals and to describe the large-scale communication management concept entitled, "EPIC-Economic Progress through International Communication, The United States Government."

The term, *communication,* is used here in its broad sense to mean the transference of knowledge from one individual to another; and the *information* in an information system is used to mean knowledge being communicated.

The basic premise is simple and well known to all of us:

- A healthy, expanding national economy requires a dynamic, progressive interrelationship between Government, business, labor, and education.
- These national economic forces are interacting with their counterparts in other nations at an ever-increasing rate.
- The effectiveness of the dispersed decision-making and organizational activity involved depends upon the timeliness and adequacy of the information which predicates them.

The development of a global management information system to satisfy these requirements is obviously a vast, extremely complex, and infinitely difficult task. It will take a long time to accomplish and will require considerable, coordinated effort in government ,in the private sector, and between the two. I am not now referring to the need for improved hardware or software. I *am* referring to the need to make better use of existing resources and manpower. I *am* referring to the need to transfer information systematically from time, geographic, language, and cultural points of generation to time, geographic, language and cultural points of usefulness, with basic regard for the catalytic impact such information would have on making profitable management decisions.

Time and world events are moving swiftly. We cannot afford to sit still, nor have we done so. We have recognized the need to unify and to systematize our global scientific and technological communication, and appropriate steps are being taken in this direction. We have recognized the need to unify and to systematize our intelligence, foreign affairs, medical, regulatory, and defense communication, and steps are being taken in these directions. It is time for us to consider the national interest involved and to take appropriate steps to unify and systematize our international commercial-economic communication. Let me briefly describe the government aspect.

EXPANSION OF FOREIGN TRADE IS VITAL TO ECONOMIC GROWTH AND STABILITY

American commitments in foreign nations–both military and economic assistance–upon which the success of our foreign policy depends can be underwritten only by an expansion of United States exports.

Since 1958, the trade balance has not been large enough to support our commitments. Only twice since then has there been an improvement in the balance of payments position, and both of those were caused by temporary factors.

One certain way to eliminate the balance of payments deficit and staunch the outflow of gold is to increase our exports.

Over three million American jobs are dependent upon exports. An increase in exports would lead to increased employment in every State since every State shares in the employment created by export industries.

A less tangible but equally important product of exports is the guarantee they bring of United States presence in critical areas of the world. The Soviet Union, fully aware of this, has been pursuing a vigorous program of economic penetration of foreign markets. The competition in foreign markets is as important as other, more obvious forms of U.S.-U.S.S.R. competition.

FAILURE TO INCREASE EXPORTS SUFFICIENTLY IS A MATTER OF URGENT NATIONAL POLICY

Recent government figures show that the volume of world trade has increased 306.4 percent since 1946, 19.4 percent since 1960.

The United States share of exports represented 30.7 percent of the total world trade in 1946, 22.8 percent in 1960, and is 17.2 percent today. Today our exports account for only 4 percent of our gross national product, the lowest percentage of any industrialized country.

World competition has grown stronger.

- The Common Market countries today control 27.8 percent of world trade. Within the protective tariff barriers of those nations and 13 other economic communities, industrial strength is growing and goods are moving freely to expanding markets. American businessmen are finding it increasingly difficult to compete from outside the tariff walls and are establishing plants overseas–draining off potential American jobs and profits.
- Since 1945, 32 nations have established merchant marines, a clear indication of their determination to move their raw materials in their own vessels to build up foreign exchanges.

- Russia regards world trade as the wide door to increasing its influence and prestige in developing nations. Recent estimates made by the House Judiciary Committee indicate the Soviet merchant marine will be the equal of ours by 1965 or 1966—and double ours by 1970.

In response to such compelling economic forces, the government instituted measures to strengthen the domestic economy and to stabilize the declining United States international economic posture. The government, among other efforts, established at an estimated cost in excess of $6 billion a year, its:

- Policy to strengthen the domestic economy and to relieve poverty-stricken areas through legislation of the Area Redevelopment Act (1961);
- Policy to achieve full domestic employment through legislation of the Manpower Development and Training Act of 1962;
- Policy to close the Government-Business gap by Presidential and other efforts and by establishment of the Federal Executive Boards;
- National Export Expansion Programs and legislation of the Trade Expansion Act of 1962;
- Policy to assist the economic development of friendly nations through legislation of the Act for International Development of 1961 and the Foreign Assistance Act of 1962, and is providing support and leadership to 55 intergovernmental economic organizations; and its
- Policy to provide improved global commercial communication facilities and technology through legislation of the Communications Satellite Act of 1962.

Analysis of these compelling and responsive economic forces clearly indicates that achievement of national and international goals depends in great part upon the accelerated expansion of American exports and other forms of international business. In many cases, domestic and foreign business activity are so delicately intertwined as to be inseparable.

NOT ENOUGH UNITED STATES INDUSTRIES EXPORT

One of the compelling reasons for disinterest, timidity or uncertainty on the part of potential American exporters is a lack of pertinent information on foreign markets. They will not willingly risk their capital on ventures surrounded by question marks.

Problems of obtaining reliable export and marketing information are pressing and rapidly getting worse. The volume of material to be handled, sorted, and transmitted is increasing at an ever-increasing rate. It is not well organized or classified and is in many different languages. The problem of not having the appropriate information available to the appropriate individual at the appropriate time is one of the major delimiting factors in the growth of American international business.

It is significant to note that of some 325,000 manufacturers in the United States, only about 15,000 sell their products in foreign markets, and about 4,000 of these account for about 85 percent of the sales. Obviously, the potential exists for increased foreign trade by a much larger number of United States manufacturers.

ECONOMIC PROGRESS THROUGH INTERNATIONAL COMMUNICATION

A scientifically organized worldwide information processing system that will provide the individual businessman with the knowledge upon which to base rational decisions is suggested as a means to stimulate American exports and American participation in foreign markets. This involves individuals generating information, not knowing who the recipients may be, and recipients who are widely separated from the authors by time, geography, culture, or language. The suggested system would be designed to close the communication gap between the businessman seeking information, not knowing where, when, or by whom it may have been generated, and the individual who produces information not knowing where, when, or by whom it will be needed.

The government through its numerous international commercial, economic, and export expansion programs, using its steadily improving communication facilities, is in the best position to obtain, and provide businessmen, with information they need to take advantage of foreign trade opportunities. Some 268 Foreign Service posts in 116 countries and 33 departments, agencies, and commissions are involved in programs which produce and use information vital to decision-making by American business firms. (See Fig. 1.)

Unfortunately, however, the American businessman is not getting this information, not getting it fast enough, or in a manner most useful to him.

The transference of commercial-economic information in the government and by the government to the business community is now an indirect, delayed process, and is expensive. It involves the production of information without adequate knowledge of, or regard for, end-users' requirements. The rapidly changing international business environment complicates the problem further. Language, culture, and other local impediments complicate the problem even more. Finally, the information

268 - FOREIGN SERVICE POSTS
8 - UNITED STATES MISSIONS
55 - INTERGOVERNMENTAL ORGANIZATIONS
116 - COUNTRIES

697 - CULTURAL, DEFENSE, ECONOMIC, POLITICAL, SCIENTIFIC, TECHNOLOGICAL, and SOCIAL SUBJECTS
7,500 - INDUSTRY and PRODUCT GROUP SUBJECTS

10 - GLOBAL COMMUNICATION NETWORKS
7 - FEDERAL COMMUNICATION CENTERS

33 - FEDERAL DEPARTMENTS, AGENCIES, and COMMISSIONS

430 - MANUFACTURING INDUSTRIES
325,000 - MANUFACTURERS
470 - TRADE, FINANCE, TRANSPORTATION, and other INDUSTRIES
900 - NATIONAL INDUSTRY ASSOCIATIONS
2,000 - NATIONAL TRADE ASSOCIATIONS

Figure 1. Composition of the International Commercial-Economic Communication Complex.

itself is highly perishable and subject to competition. A trade opportunity, for example, may be dead by the time the information is dispatched to the U.S. from a Foreign Service post.

Research shows that the main failure to provide timely, accurate and useful information to businessmen is that present commercial-economic information processing procedures are inadequate, loosely constructed, loosely integrated, and heterogeneous, and the information being sought by a business man oftentimes is fragmented and scattered throughout various Federal agencies.

In 1961, the Department of State distributed some 21,800,000 copies of Foreign Service commercial-economic airgrams and telegrams to 28 Federal agencies. In 1963, it distributed 31,200,000 copies to 33 agencies. Despite these volume increases, however, communication gaps continue to exist between foreign markets and Foreign Service posts, between Foreign Service posts and the Federal agencies in Washington, within the agencies, between the agencies, and between the Government in general and the business community. So that, while Government officials and businessmen are overwhelmed with information that is only partially

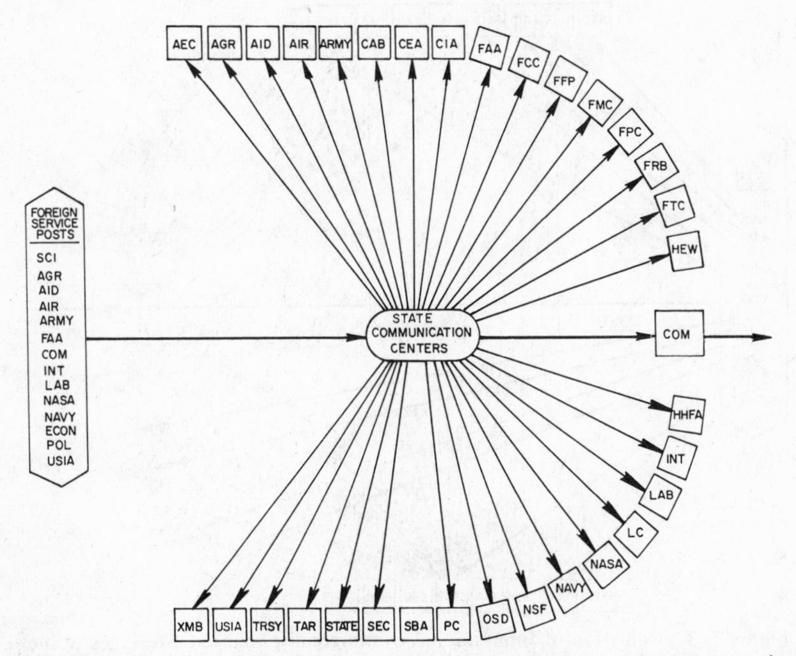

Figure 2. Government Agencies Receiving Copies of Department of State International Commercial-Economic Messages.

relevant, or not relevant at all, to their particular interest, they are deprived of information developed at great cost to the government which they do require to carry out their respective responsibilities effectively. (See Figs. 2 and 3.)

Federal agencies have found that 60–65 percent of the time of professional government analysts is spent in sorting, filing, and searching for data, rather than in the critical research, analysis, and briefing which would provide the information needed by government and by business.

The commercial-economic information collected by the government is for the most part nonclassified and nonproprietary. It is an important national resource. The question is, how can this available information—which is public property—be made accessible in usable form on a timely basis to those who need it?

Some operations research has been done on this information transfer problem. A preliminary survey report entitled "A Proposed Coordinated System for International Commercial-Economic Communication in the Government" was prepared in 1962 and was published by the U.S. Senate Subcommittee on Reorganization and International Organizations.

This effort was followed by the development of a concept designed to

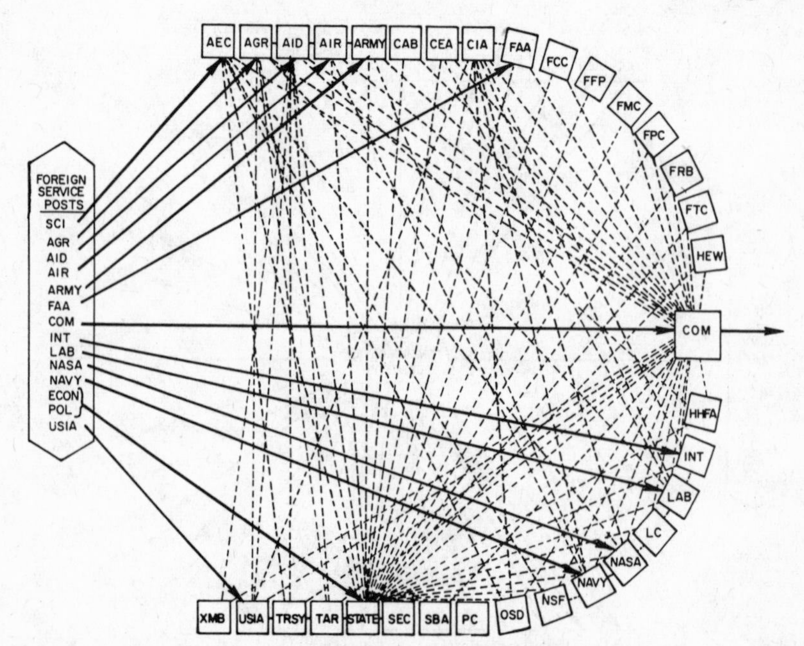

Figure 3. Transmission of International Commercial-Economic Messages to the Government and Exchanges of Information (Indicative) Between 33 Departments and Agencies.

close, in evolutionary steps, the various information transference gaps. It recognizes the need to apply advanced techniques for the scientific organization and management of global communication systems. It is entitled "EPIC–Economic Progress through International Communication," the subject of this presentation.

The EPIC operations research revealed the necessity to define and apply certain differences in several prevalent management of information system concepts:

- Substantive information processing as an integral management activity versus administrative data processing as a "housekeeping" support function;
- The information versus the media and methods used to transmit it;
- Dissemination of common interest information versus dissemination of limited interest information;
- Timely, initial information dissemination versus efficient, subsequent retrieval; and
- Data/information retrieval versus document retrieval.

The EPIC operations research also tested the combined effectiveness of:

- Block diagram analysis;
- Stratified system analysis;
- The incidence matrix (Figs. 4 & 5); and
- Successive approximation.

The application of these management techniques will be shown in the charts to follow.

The EPIC concept emphasizes the need for:

- A common-use terminology;
- Effective organization for optimum, integrated information inputs to serve optimum end-user requirements in the government and in the business community;
- Interrelated unity of interdependent communication operations at the Foreign Service posts and the federal agencies;
- Effective use of the National Communications System and the Federal Telecommunications System, and, as feasible, the developing Communication Satellite System;
- Controlled collection, analysis, and discriminating dissemination of information to government organization units and business;
- Critical pathway processing of information by organization units and through communication links;

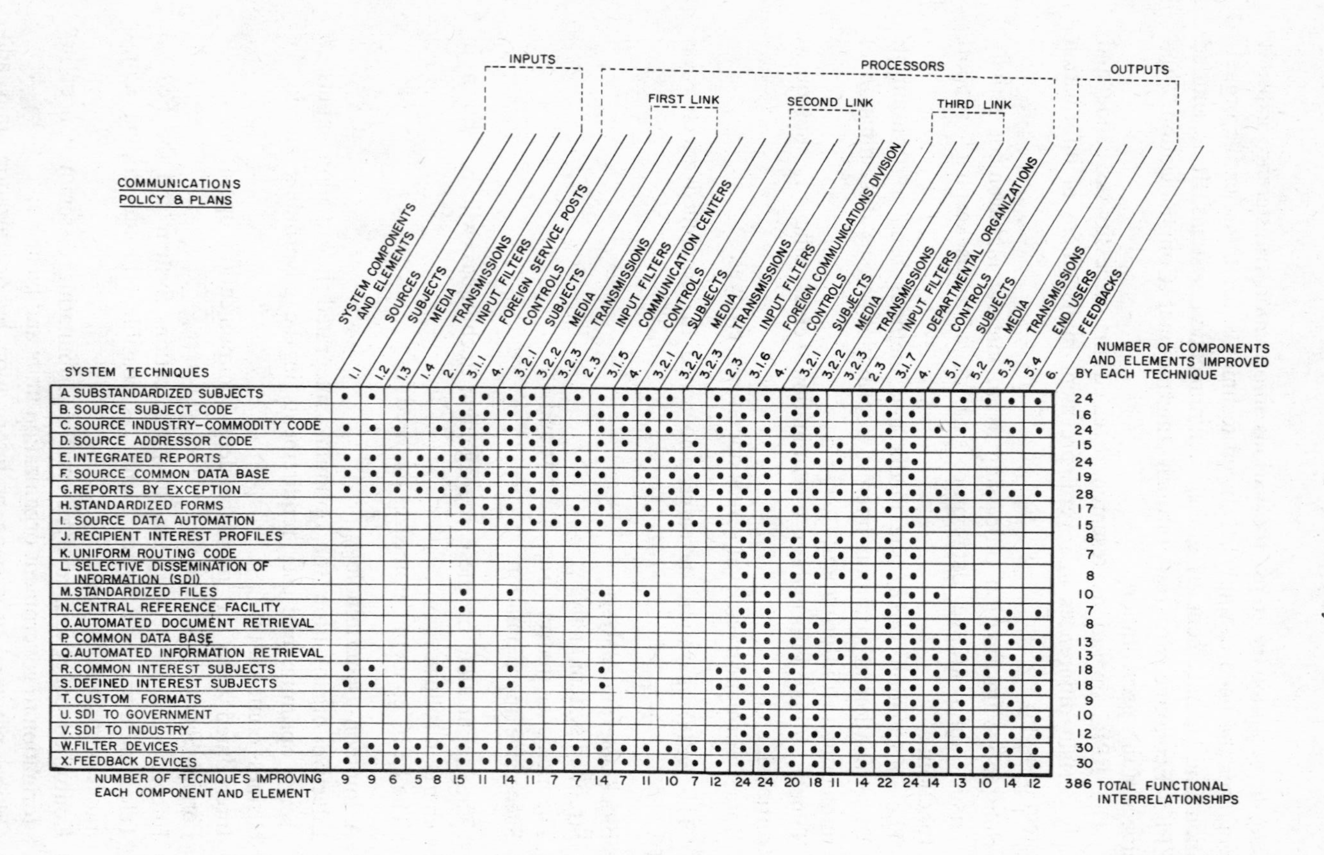

Figure 4. Organization and Administration of an Integrated Communication System Functional Interrelationships Between System Components, Elements and Techniques.

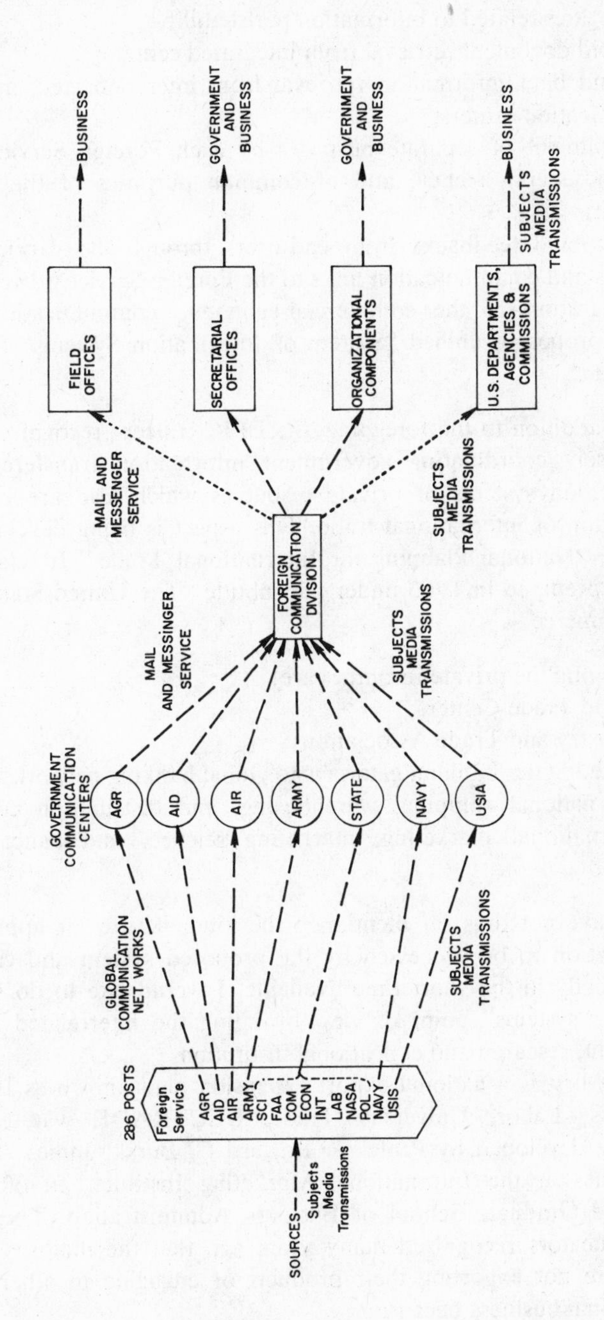

Figure 5. Organization and Administration of an Integrated Communication System, System Components and Elements.

- Priorities related to information perishability;
- Rapid document retrieval from integrated centers;
- Rapid data/information retrieval from interconnected, automated communication centers;
- Fulfillment of separate purposes by each Foreign Service post and by each federal agency, and of common purposes of the entire government;
- Integrated feedbacks from end-users through the various organization units and communication links to the Foreign Service posts; and
- Integration of the commercial-economic communication system into the proposed, unified "System of Information Systems" for the government.

In addition to the foregoing, the EPIC concept recognizes the necessity of closely coordinating government information transferences with the information systems of private resources which also are essential to the expansion of international trade. This aspect is being developed under the subtitle "National Planning for International Trade." It relates to another aspect prepared in 1963 under the subtitle "The United States Department of Commerce."

Among the private resources are:

- World Trade Centers;
- Industry and Trade Associations;
- United States banking gateways to global banking networks;
- International shipping, warehousing, and distribution companies; and
- International marketing, marketing science, and educational institutions.

I have not thus far mentioned the kind, nature, or application of the information to be processed by the proposed system and can do so only very briefly in the short time available. I would like to do so indicatively from a "systems" point of view by citing the interrelated efforts of two nonprofit, research and educational institutions.

The first is a national export expansion plan known as BLUTRADE—Business, Labor, University Trade. BLUTRADE was conceived and is being developed by Professor Edward C. Bursk, James A. Hagler, and colleagues at the International Marketing Institute, an off-shoot of the Harvard Graduate School of Business Administration. These researchers and educators recognized many years ago that the majority of American firms are not exporting their products or engaging in other forms of international business because:

- They are unaware of the profit potentials;
- They do not know the location of overseas markets;
- They do not know how to analyze foreign marketing opportunities;
- They are overwhelmed by the problems of distance, language, culture, international shipping and financing; and, in general,
- They are reluctant to make investments which they consider risky.

The IMI researchers also tested the applicability of the Marketing Mix for marketing analysis abroad. The Marketing Mix is an interrelated set of 16 factors for conducting marketing analyses, such as: competition, consumer attitudes and habits, governmental controls, trade attitudes and methods, advertising, pricing, etc. The Mix was developed and tested in the United States from some 40,000 actual cases in business administration since 1921. The IMI researchers, reviewing some 4,500 cases in business administration in other countries and by other techniques, determined that the Marketing Mix is essentially as applicable in selling overseas as in domestic markets.

IMI took this know-how to the grass roots of American industry less than a year ago in two pilot projects—one in Worcester, Massachusetts and the other in Hartford, Connecticut. Studies of local industries and their potential to export made by University of Connecticut and Assumption College researchers under IMI guidance indicated that two out of five manufacturers in the two cities have exportable products, but only about one in every three of these firms are exporting.

The method used was (1) to marshal all local resources, including government, labor, banking, business associations, chambers of commerce, and the universities, and (2) to provide export training and marketing guidance through a series of seminars and discussions with individual company managers. One estimate of possible results is that the exploitation of export possibilities by Hartford firms could add 1200 jobs and additional sales of $10 million to $15 million a year in that city alone. By virtue of the interest it has thus attracted, IMI has been requested to consider BLUTRADE programs for some 65 cities in the United States. It has deferred doing so until completion of the pilot projects.

The communication importance of the IMI plan is emphasized by the fact that its main thrust is directed toward individual business firms, thereby providing the basis for closing four significant gaps in the national export expansion effort:

- The need to establish information requirements for individual firms;
- The need to transfer information to points where it is required;
- The profitable use of the information; and

- The need to generate integrated feedbacks from end-users of the information.

The second effort refers to the work of Dr. Wendell R. Smith and Michael H. Halbert at the Marketing Science Institute in Philadelphia. These men and their colleagues are vigorously striving to establish marketing as a science in conjunction with other similar efforts. Among other factors, they have recognized the importance to managers of being continuously informed on changing foreign market forces and changing applications of marketing techniques, and of the need for a well-ordered common-use terminology such as those established and being improved in the physical, biological, and medical sciences.

By citing these examples, I do not mean to overlook in any way the significant value of the work being done by such organizations as the Domestic and International Business units of the U.S. Department of Commerce, the Small Business Administration, the American Management Association, the American Marketing Association, and many others.

I would now like to invite your attention to a few diagrams and charts which illustrate, by example, current information processing procedures in the government.

VISUAL PROJECTIONS AND EXPLANATORY REMARKS

1. The Block Diagram as an analytical tool.
2. The United States Government as a processor of international commercial-economic information.
3. Composition of the international commercial-economic communication complex.
4. Federal agency responsibilities in the expansion of international trade.
5. Federal agencies receiving copies of Department of State commercial-economic messages.
6. Transmissions of foreign commercial-economic information and exchanges of information (indicative) between Federal agencies.
7. A Federal agency as a processor of international commercial-economic information.
8. Processing organization units.
9. A first-level stratification of inputs to a Federal agency.
10. Transmission pathways for telegraphic message inputs.
11. Transmission pathways for written message and printed inputs.
12. Flow chart of reproducible message transmissions to organization units.

13. Organization unit outputs.
14. Forms simplification and standardization.
15. System components and elements.
16. The System Index.
17. Functional interrelationships between system components, elements, and techniques–the incidence matrix as an instrument of communication management for controlled research and development.

The White House Conference on Export Expansion last fall, the "Kennedy Round" of negotiations on General Agreements on Tariffs and Trade now taking place in Geneva, and the concurrent United Nations Conference on Trade Assistance and Development attended by 121 nations and described as the largest international conference in history, reflect the rising global tide of international trade and the rapidly changing international business environment. The growth, or perhaps even the survival, of American business firms depends upon their ability to keep pace with, or ahead of, the accompanying surge of competition both at home and abroad.

I hope I have been able in this short time to show to some extent that our economy, to remain strong and to grow, requires the support of a communication network which will provide management information to business firms so they can:

- Expand present foreign sales; or
- Emerge into world markets; and thereby
- Stimulate the domestic economy;
- Reverse the relative decline of our world economic leadership; and
- Help offset Soviet economic competition in free and developing nations.

A well-known precedent for the development of this type of communication network is manifested in improvements now being made in scientific and technological communication. Efforts to affect closer coordination of scientific and technological communication in the government, and between the government and the scientific and technical community, as shown in part by other speakers at this Institute, will gradually provide improved support for the achievement of national goals, and large-scale, wasteful efforts and expenditures will gradually be reduced.

The initial steps taken to improve scientific and technological communication in the United States are essentially the steps which can be, and should be, taken to improve our commercial-economic communication. We have noted the large number of Federal agencies involved in commercial-economic activities, and that no one agency has the scope of responsibility or authority essential for effective over-all communication improvement. It is necessary, therefore, for coordinated action to be taken at the highest levels of the government.

This is a case in which the profit motive and the national interest coincide completely.

PART IV

IMPROVING THE STRUCTURING, CONTENT, AND USEFULNESS OF DATA

USE OF MATHEMATICAL AND ANALYTICAL TOOLS IN ORGANIZING DATA

AUGUSTUS C. JOHNSON
Booz, Allen Applied Research Corp., Bethesda, Md.

This paper summarizes and surveys some methods that seem to be appropriate for organizing data and which can be loosely grouped into the category of mathematical, statistical, and analytical techniques.

We are sometimes a little bit handicapped by the fact that we don't have an acceptable definition of mathematics. This may be a handicap or it may be a benefit because this means that perhaps you need not be too rigorous about what you call mathematics. It means that you can identify just about anything you want as mathematics if it has a number in it, or a pattern.

Mathematical science adopts, generally, two viewpoints which we usually call theoretical and applied or pure and applied mathematics. If you need examples of these definitions, you referred in high school algebra to "number" problems and to "word" problems. I think that this distinction can be followed all the way through the entire mathematical discipline. Looking at such an equation as $Y = MX + B$, we can consider it from these two different viewpoints. From the "pure" mathematics viewpoint, we might try to develop a set of rules under which one could manipulate these equations to develop a theoretical mathematical science, which will be internally consistent and "elegant" as the mathematicians say, but which need not bear any resemblance at all to the outside world. Of course, the other half of this is the "applied" one. When you write the equation $Y = MX + B$ you also realize that this could be an expression for some relationship between physical quantities. It could be an expression for some economic relationship between prices and unit quantities. It could also be a geometrical relationship showing what a line looks like. We have applied mathematics when a relationship between real-world quantities behaves in the same way as a relationship between mathematical quantities. One of the great advantages of this, of course, is that there is a tremendous volume of theoretical mathematics, statistics, and analytical techniques, which is available for application any place where one can find a match between some part of this theoretical body and some phenomenon in the real world.

I would like to discuss today some of the approaches and efforts that have been made by different persons to establish matches between portions of the information or data problem and portions of this body of theoretical mathematical structure. Many of the approaches have been very successful and very productive, others are still very tentative. There also have been, of course, failures and I think some of the most promising are still in the very early stages. I would like to examine a few of these with you and discuss them in fairly nontechnical terms to see what they promise for us.

In the first place, there is the statistical organization of quantitative measurements in many fields of application. One of the problems that one incurs, if he is an active practitioner (particularly if he is a classical statistician), is the habit scientists, engineers, observers, and experimenters have of deluging him with bushel baskets of data with the request for him to analyze the data for meaning. A good deal of my own exposure in the last five years has been to the Space effort and this has many examples of what I have stated. There is often a tremendous body of observational data, a good deal collected under very rigorous circumstances and capable of being interpreted in very accurate and meaningful ways, which has been taken by people operating in this field, which will probably never contribute anything important to science. The reason for this, in many cases, is either because it is redundant, or because it has large gaps in its coverage. In case after case, you have information on both sides of a critical point, but none at the critical one. There is just so much information that you just don't know what to do with it.

This is the position that almost all of us, particularly in the computer or data processing sciences, have found ourselves in time and again. I remember when the first large data-processing system was installed at the Pentagon, I was invited to inspect it by the Director of Statistical Services of the Air Force. As we were walking through the room, a hand truck was being wheeled out, stacked with printout four feet deep—so much paper that it would take a lifetime to read. This emphasizes the type of problem we are confronted with. In many such cases, we are standing under Niagara Falls with a teaspoon trying to decide what to do with all the information that is being directed at us.

There is a statistical technique which attacks this problem very directly and very successfully. This consists of designing your experiment before collecting your data. In simple terms, this implies that before you take any data at all, you are sure of what you are looking for and furthermore, what you are going to do with it when you get it. This is a very simple concept. I believe that there is perhaps more room for improvement in this one particular area than in anything else that may be involved in the data collection process.

A few simple examples will serve to illustrate the cardinal point. Suppose that a person is interested in some aspects of a varying physical quantity. For instance, this might concern a satellite. The measurement might involve magnetic fields strengths or radiation variations. In general, you would like to develop a functional relationship between the pertinent variables. The classical approach is to illustrate the relationship by drawing a curve. You require enough points so that you can draw at least a rough curve. Later you may wish to interpolate on the curve and find a new point, to enable you to predict what will happen in future cases. You may also wish to establish or clarify some sort of a physical hypothesis about a relationship between the quantities represented. If you simply gather all possible information and attempt to analyze, invariably, you note that at certain points the data "bunches" while at other points you have none. Invariably, if you don't plan, you will obtain many times as many observations in one cell or unit of time as in another. Of course, the confidence that you can place on your results depends not only upon the number of observations but also on their consistency and the completeness of their coverage. You may have the experience of having insufficient data; hence requiring repeating of the experiment. Practitioners of experimental design insist that it is better to collect just the amount of data that will give the greatest confidence than to start right in collecting before you really know what is your ultimate aim. One way to start on the right track is to go through a dry run of your entire process including your statistical analysis before starting actual experimentation.

First and foremost, we must keep in view the validity and the acceptability of the end result. Next in importance is, of course, the cost. If you collect unnecessary data, every unnecessary fact collected not only will cost you money to collect, but also will clog up the entire data processing mechanism. The thing that must be guarded against is what the statisticians call the "PARC" principle or "Planning After the Research is Completed".

There are two or three rather specific disciplines, that are fairly well advanced, that can be adapted to almost any kind of a data gathering and analysis operation. They may be employed with quite good effect with no further development required. One of these very useful disciplines is Information Theory. This theory resulted from the initiative of the communication scientists, and seeks to quantify the usually very vague idea of what we mean by Information. So far, a good many theorems, a good many concepts have been derived from Information Theory. Many of these attempt to explain what is possible and what is not. We do not always have practical rules to apply this theory, but there is a good possibility that future progress will be faster.

In this theory, information is defined as that which removes uncertainty, and the quantity of information in a message is measured by the amount of uncertainty which exists before the message is received, minus the amount of uncertainty which exists after the message is received. Let us probe deeper by looking into what can be used as a quantitative measure of information so defined, based on perhaps the simplest kind of information delivery system that you can imagine and that is a system having only two choices. If we toss a coin, either heads or tails will appear, presumably with equal probability. At the moment our uncertainty is therefore that we know that it is either one or the other, and it is going to take one very simple observation to find out what it is. The amount of information that you get in determining whether it is heads or tails, is defined as one bit of information, on binary digit, one choice between two equally probable alternatives. Now, as you develop the entire idea of choice among alternatives, you find that you may have more than just two alternatives and you may have situations in which some of the choices are considerably more likely than others. It is entirely possible in a straightforward simple algebraic method to express all these situations in terms of the basic concept of a bit of information. In other words, each of these situations is expressible by some binary equation, where a certain number of individual choices between two alternatives are possible. For another example, we might consider a message which is made up of the two digits 0 and 1. Each digit then conveys one bit of information, since before we see it we are uncertain as to whether it is 0 or 1, but after we see it this uncertainty is removed. We might also consider some other kind of a code which has more digits than this, such as perhaps the alphabet, or a set of ten decimal digits, or an augmented alphabet where you have both of those and maybe a few additional symbols. We could refer to a string or combination of these symbols as a message, not restricted to ordinary English words. In the broadest possible sense, a message may be a document; it may be the code or index to a document; it may be any pattern or combination of symbols which transmits information. In each instance, there is a message content measured by the number of equal binary choices to which it is equivalent.

One of the complications of this theory is that every such message, every such situation, is imbedded in a total of information which exists before the message is received. When one considers information in a sense of relieving uncertainty (removing uncertainty in the mind of the receiver), one has to consider all *possible* assumptions, all the agreements, existing between the person or facility or institution which sends the message and that which receives. Such a situation might be the one shown in the movie "Dr. Strangelove." In this instance, the airbase sent a message to the bomber in flight consisting of a very small number of digits. Upon receiving these digits, the captain of the aircraft opened a safe, removed a group of envelopes which had code numbers and the names of the people to whom the envelopes were to be handed, such as the pilot, the navigator, and the bombardier. He then handed one of these envelopes to each. Upon being opened individually, they were shown to contain full war plans with a great deal of information. The information as finally delivered did not possess much uncertainty.

At first, there was uncertainty as to the choice among the numbered sets of envelopes. The zero choice meant no action. Thus, by receiving only one message, with a certain amount of content in it, a great deal of information in the ordinary sense was transmitted. We ought to realize that when we talk about transmissions, there is inferred a whole set of further agreements, considerable additional understanding among the persons using the systems. This can be carried a little further if you consider the fact that if we are talking about one particular branch of science or one particular branch of knowledge of any kind (such as oceanography or physics), there is a whole general agreement among those practicing in this field as to the meaning of various terms and the way in which they are used. This is one of the chief problems confronting communications between people. What frequently makes the operations somewhat lacking in rigor is the lack of general agreements. Unless the agreements are precise, the message is not rigorous.

The fact that we can, through information theory, discover the maximum explicit content of any certain message does not mean that we can properly convey all these understood agreements. We cannot agree on the validity of the picture which is built up in the mind of the beholder or in the actual total amount of information conveyed unless we also consider all the implied information that is in the message. The agreements which exist, before the message is sent, are at least as important as the content of the message itself. So, this is something that we must explore.

To give a better idea about the manner of applying this technique to other codes, we might consider four digits, A, B, C, and D. To determine the information content of a message using these we should first consider the way in which these can be interpreted as a number of bits of information. First of all, with only four digits, one has only to call them 0, 0; 0, 1; 1, 0; 1, 1; which are all the four combinations of 0 and 1. By doing this, a code is derived, giving the binary equivalent of this particular alphabet.

Information theory directs itself to the question of what can be done and what is the most efficient way to do certain things. It addresses itself to the question of how many bits of information can be handled by a channel. When one talks about channels, one could mean either a radio channel of a certain definite bandwidth or other familiar communications channels. But a channel could also be a transmitted document, it could be any sort of carrier which conveys information. One of the chief interests today is the adaptation of computers to the communications process. A very good measure of the volume which can pass through a computer is, of course, the number of bits of information which have to be handled, the same terminology which we are using in communications.

We have seen how the capacity of a channel is defined by information theory. However, the theory will not tell you how to approach this ultimate capacity. It does specify that you can carry a certain number of bits of information per second in a particular channel, with a certain level of confidence. While this will help you in designing systems by indicating that the channel should not be called upon for more than it can carry, it may not provide adequate information as to how to approach that limit.

The type of coding so far discussed assumes that all symbols are of equal importance. If, in fact, the message frequencies of the symbols are not equal, it may well be desirable to assign the simplest code to the one which appears most often.

If, for instance one starts with an assemblage of a very large number of units and desires to adopt a code which will lead him to one particular unit in this assembly in the most efficient way, he might divide the assembly into two groups each equally likely to be consulted and code one group 0 and the other group 1. If he then divides each group into two subgroups in a similar way and continues until it is possible to arrive at any unit by the most efficient coding method, the smallest possible number of binary choices. This method is feasible for coding messages in the ordinary sense and also for many applications in filing, retrieval and sorting.

One of the common systems of coding, of course, that we are most familiar with is the English language. The English language is a rather inefficient sort of transmission device in this particular sense. It requires a very large bandwidth to send clear English text, either through a transmission channel or through a document or anything else. Of course, the classical word for the surplus between the most efficient and the actual is the redundancy of the system.

Redundancy is not necessarily a bad thing because, if in fact, you are interested in making sure that the message is delivered with a certain amount of accuracy or confidence, redundancy can be a very useful thing. Note that in a perfectly efficient code, every possible combination has a meaning, so that an error in transmission produces a combination with the wrong meaning. Therefore, a code might be constructed by using first, the most efficient code (that is, the code that will transmit the most through a given channel), and then deliberately adding redundancy, which permits the existence of unacceptable combinations. In other words, there are combinations of digits which simply are not meaningful to the receiver. This means that if a mistake is made by transposition, or erroneously sending a zero when a one should have been transmitted (or vice versa), the error would be discovered because an unacceptable combination of digits would be rejected by the receiver.

Clear English has a great deal of redundancy in it. The estimates vary from 50 to 80 percent. The reason that it varies so widely is that it depends a great deal on the underlying assumptions and the agreements between the people who use it. You can illustrate this in several very interesting ways. It is said by the theoreticians in linguistics that a language must have a redundancy of approximately 50 percent if you are to be able to write interesting and workable crossword puzzles in that language. You know that after you have completed a few words in a crossword puzzle, you can usually guess at the remainder. This means that if you can tell what the word is after you know only half of its letters, half of the letters are surplus and they add nothing to the efficiency of the operation. There is a purpose to this redundancy, however. It does keep you from making mistakes and it makes sure that when you see a gross error in a transmitted message, you are very apt to detect it.

A game that you might play is for two persons to sit down with one of them looking at a text of some sort with the other one trying to guess what it says. He attempts to guess it letter by letter and the only thing that the first person can say is "Yes" or "No." If you are knowledgeable about letter frequency, you might start with "e" and go through the alphabet in order of frequency of occurrence. Probably at the first attempt, you will be relatively inefficient. Beginning with the second letter, you have a much better chance of correctly guessing. If the first one turned out to be "q" for instance, you would probably guess immediately that the second one was "u" if it is English. There are also other correlations that are not quite as obvious but which are fairly likely.

Some very careful experiments have been accomplished in this manner with the discovery that on the average it takes a fraction between three and four guesses for the average person to guess all of the letters of the word. As the message becomes longer and longer, the number of guesses per word gets lower and lower because, at least in theory, you can begin to pick up the subject, begin to analyze the style and the syntax. This redundancy is common to most languages, but is not equally distributed. In a natural language, you may find that the redundancy which enables you to check errors and make corrections is distributed in such a way that all the redundancy does not help to pick out errors. Some errors may be detected but you may have a great deal more redundancy in one part of the message than in another. The scientific construction of codes endeavors to make sure that you buy all of the rigor, all of the accuracy possible, by distributing redundancy scientifically among the various parts of the message. This is an application of this particular theory.

There are other general categories of mathematical application which are of some interest. There are entire branches of mathematics which have nothing whatever to do with quantity or with number or with size. What they really are concerned with is the geometrical order in which things occur. The whole area which encompasses graph theory, and networks falls into this category. These have some applications which are very pertinent to information organization and retrieval. One such application is illustrated by a system designed in Europe by the European Atomic Energy Agency. This particular model has been called the "general diagram" theory of organizing a body of knowledge. This simply means that for a particular area of knowledge, such as one of the social or physical sciences, a satisfactory description of the accepted structure of the body of knowledge must first be agreed upon. The theory assumes that in any accepted body of knowledge, there are a certain number of crucial terms, critical terms, terms which really categorize the area of knowledge. If we are talking about physics, these terms might be concepts such as Force, or Magnetic Field. If you are talking about psychological applications, we might be referring to different kinds of intelligence, different kinds of apperception, different aspects of almost anything that you would care to mention. The links between them always describe relationships of some sort. In general, the terms will be either nouns or adjectives, or sometimes adverbs, while the connecting links of language are prepositions or other words which show the relationship of one term to another term.

It is believed to be possible, and some experiments have succeeded on a limited scale, in setting up networks which encompass a certain body of knowledge fairly accurately, described in such a way that when you have a document or message, referring to a part of the total content, it can be mechanically matched. You thus try to match this document, which contains certain interconnected words, with the general diagram to determine whether it is part of the body of knowledge set forth by the diagram. In a practical sense, this can be used to answer the question of whether certain documents refer to the same body of knowledge, and thus do in fact belong in a particular bibliography. We can also determine, perhaps, whether or not two documents overlap enough so that one is redundant. Also, by carrying this further and analyzing on a theoretical basis, it might well be that we will evolve new methods which could contribute a good deal more to our insight into how knowledge is organized in the human brain. This is indeed promising. It is possible, at present, however, by means of an entirely mechanical process, involving no human judgment, to take any given document, classify it, check it against a diagram and tell what the correspondence is between the two and develop perhaps an index or degree of relevancy.

Another method (called *Syntol*), very much the same as the one discussed, refines the relationships considerably more. This generally separates the terms of ordinary scientific language, natural language, into artificial nodes and links. It reduces the number of different kinds of links to perhaps four or five. Furthermore, the relationships which can exist between terms of a language are a little more refined and a little more theoretical.

The graph theory, which is a well-developed branch of theoretical mathematics, provides a set of tools for analyzing graphs. It usually starts at one node and counts the number of extended links to the next node. It sets up a pattern for the entire network describing that network in such a way as to classify and match it against other networks to see whether in fact this is the same network or a different one. If you take a very large number of terms and a very large number of links, it is entirely possible to assemble them in such a way that the same terms and the same links will produce a new network that can't easily be recognized by the unaided eye. This is one of the problems that is being quite successfully attacked.

The idea of spatial or pattern relationship, imbedded in our language, is a very hopeful sign for applying such new techniques. There is a fairly good example of an application of mathematics pertinent here. This originates from fairly elementary ideas and utilizes very straightforward methods in a very imaginative way. Quite a number of investigations start out by taking a set of documents, or messages, and simply coding them. This is accomplished by numbering each technical term, noun, adjective, that is found in the document and inserting a one or a zero in a matrix indicating whether this term occurs in this particular document. Simply a form of record-keeping. Another thing that might be done is to count the words which occur in each document, counting the number of times that each word recurs and you put that number in the cell, the number "A" which indicates that in document No. 4, term No. 3 occurs "A" times, something like that. Matrix algebra can certainly be applied to this, as well as to many of its extensions. We can, for instance, set an index of the general correspondence or the general pertinency of document No. 1 to document No. 5 by any one of several varieties of similarities. Perhaps the simplest way to do it is to count the number of times that the number one occurs in the first column at the same time that it occurs in the fifth column. Those who are involved in bibliographic classification know, however, that there are many pitfalls between simple statements and applications.

There are other things which you can do which have a slightly higher level of sophistication than simply ascertaining correlation between sets of columns or rows. For instance, you can find out whether individual terms bear a relationship to each other, so that two of the rows may be related. It may well turn out that one row is completely redundant. In other words, if row five appears in every single document that row one appears in, it may well be that one term or the other can be abandoned as being unnecessary in forming a basis for classifying.

It has been known for several years that a carefully laid out program can use automatic methods to produce fairly useful results, without skilled human intervention. This could mean that a large number of documents could be translated into machine language and fed into a computer, and that thereafter many of the steps could be accomplished automatically. The initial step is to develop a list of words which are not acceptable as classification words; the obvious ones that you think of are "the," "and," "of," etc., which don't tell you very much about the subject matter of the document. Then, the essential words which occur in the document are counted, simply word frequency by document. We make a set of cells wherein the documents are numbered across the top and the terms are numbered down the left-hand side. Then by automatic scanning, we determine whether, in fact, the documents bear correlative relationships to each other. One can then ascertain a basis for classifying documents as being similar, identical, or very different. It may be necessary to introduce an intermediate step to eliminate the synonym-homonym problem. I think that you can see that the synonym problem is somewhat easier to eliminate than the homonym because our natural language contains so many words which are used in diverse ways, making it extremely difficult to develop completely automatic rules for eliminating the different usages. It is possible to develop rules which will say that every time you read a certain word, that we are referring to the "social science" context, for instance. There are also certain words like "force," "strength," or "power," which in many of the social sciences may be considered identical. On the other hand, if you are talking about physics or engineering, they are very different. This is a very simple matter to program into a computer. You simply have a table of equivalents. When you see one word you go to its equivalent and go on through the steps in either direction.

One of the most useful things for doing experimental work in automatic retrieval systems would be a really good input system. Character recognition is still very experimental and the successful operations are rather expensive. It would be very helpful if you didn't have to sit down and key-punch a hundred thousand words on a good many documents to get a sample big enough to analyze. And finally, it would indeed be extremely useful if more could be done to show some of these analytical techniques to people who need classification systems to judge as to whether, in fact, these approaches are as promising as they seem to me.

PACKAGING, LABELING, AND FINDING EVALUATED TECHNICAL DATA

ROBERT L. BIRCH
U.S. Patent Office Library, Washington, D.C.

The originator of any body of technical data has the responsibility of making it findable, if it may later be useful. The packaging and labeling of such masses of information are basic to the problem of later recovery.

Even if the cargo of information is worth millions of dollars, if it is dumped into the informational mainstream without proper packaging and labeling, it can become merely another sandbar. If information cannot be found when needed, it will practically have ceased to exist, except as a memory.

Certain African tribes have memory-men who record the knowledge of the tribe in their memories, and can recite, hour after hour, from the history and genealogies of the group. We train our memories too little, but even at best, we could not use people to fully substitute for writings and computer tapes, we have too much data, and they are too complicated and random.

LABELING

Retrieval processes depend on packaging and labeling, and on the manner of indexing and of announcing the existence of the record. You may have a white elephant of information, very costly to prepare or duplicate, and you wish to make sure that it can be found and interpreted when needed. You may attend a meeting where colleagues express an interest in the data and in your effort to package and label them. At the invitation of the chairman, you give a short talk on informational white elephants and on how to process large bodies of evaluated technical data, without polluting the informational mainstream. A journal editor asks for your text. Then, a few months later, someone writes to you from a bureau in Washington, or from a research laboratory in India, to ask the disposition of the corpses of elephants.

This illustrates part of the labeling process, and its peculiar problems.

Labeling the parts within the mass of information can be called the "informational white-elephant anatomical nomenclature" and it will be discussed later.

PACKAGING

The package in which information is stored may be the informal talk at a meeting, a journal article, a book, or series of volumes, and on through the most extensive computer-center facilities. If the information is published in tables or compilations of tables, there may be supplemental volumes, or loose-leaf services, or tapes.

Other specialists know of the existence of this material through the grapevine, or through announcements in the specialist journals, or other announcement systems. How long it takes to learn of such material is a function of the practicality of the packaging, of the effectiveness of the labeling, and of the findability of the announcements through indexes, reference centers, and the rest of the bibliographic and data-finding apparatus. Finally, there are reference centers which accumulate these large bodies of information, embalm them, and serve them to the unsuspecting seekers after knowledge, much as the national archives process materials which are somewhat dead.

REPRESENTATIVE SOURCES

The appended list headed "Numerical Data Retrieval: Representative Publications" gives a sampling of the sort of publication already available by which the existence of data centers can be sniffed out, as the most likely place to find a certain sort of table.

For instance, the first item is *Current Research and Development in Scientific Documentation.* This is a listing, with indexes, of the various projects undertaken to make information more manageable and data more findable. It is similar to item 2, the *Directory of Continuing Numerical Projects* and to item 4, *Nonconventional Technical Information Systems in Current Use.*

Item 5, *Information Communication Practice in Industry,* is listed because it has a discussion of the designing of tables. If you are planning to produce tabulated material and find yourself at a loss about the most appropriate procedures, that chapter may be of some help. Its bibliography is also useful. The other items 6, 7, and 8, are the sort of thing that a reference librarian might be able to check as first steps in finding any sort of information needed. For instance, if you want a certain characteristic of rutile, the index shows the existence of specialized information services, or of publications which serve as guides to the existence of other tables. This is the ladder up which we must climb.

In the Appendix, the second section, "Tables," mentions other representative tabulations. For instance, item 10, Landolt-Börnstein, in German, is a shelf-yard of tables on all sorts of physical, chemical, and astronomical properties. Specialists tell me that a certain amount of this material has to be taken with a few grains of salt, because it was copied from this or copied from that. The critical tables, themselves, the International Critical Tables, which for so long were a standard of this sort of thing, were compiled from a source put out by the French, and this guide included all sorts of peculiar fossilized terminology. Here you run into the phenomenon of the "elastic ruler". At the time when certain data were accumulated, the measurements were made with a standard inch or standard meter, or what have you. If the tolerance of your research requires that the material be recalculated on the basis of a later standardization of the meter, for compatability with your other research, you still may find that the labeling of the particular tables, or the labeling of the data in a given source, was not sufficiently exact; it did not indicate whether researchers were using an inch standardized before a certain date, or one adopted later. For instance, in 1959 the United States and Great Britain standardized their inch. They decided on an inch about half way between the older British inch and the American inch. To some degree that sort of change will affect your calculations, or the compatability of your later data with the earlier data that you use; the labeling of the standards, and of the conventions, under which your instrumentation was developed is pertinent to the possible utility of whatever data you are trying to use.

If you wish to find data in Touloukian and your procedure is to look it up directly, you may first have to go through the process of learning to use this particular set of tables. A reference librarian once told me that looking in Touloukian was more work than looking up the same material in the sources that Touloukian had used. The degree to which the prejudices and the experience, and so forth of reference librarians or data center personnel will enter into and affect the selection of data, the finding of data, for you, is one of the imponderables. A more direct problem here under Touloukian is listed by the Library of Congress under "Purdue University" as the main entry: "Purdue University, Thermophysical Properties Research Center, Lafayette, Indiana."

This brings us to another question: When you are going to launch, into the informational mainstream, a shipload of tables of data, you may name the ship in some curious way which itself cannot be found. For instance, your title page on a compilation of tables may be cluttered with acknowledgement of one or more editors, a title, a sponsoring organization (two or three sponsoring organizations, perhaps) and later you attempt to keep this set up to date with loose-leaf supplements. Receiving clerks all over the country have to handle the loose-leaf supplements, and will find themselves routing this material, or losing it, depending on the ease with which they can predict, or coordinate, or remember, the destination and the main entry that was used to describe the main body of the material. For instance, if the set was filed under "Purdue" and the clerk receives three thousand publications, three thousand sheets of loose-leaf material every month, and if the only emphatic thing on the loose-leaf is "Touloukian Retrieval Guide," the clerk may have to look in a great many different places before he can find out how he filed the main body of Touloukian's materials.

The built-in confusion which is commonplace in the publication of all sorts of compilation is a major obstacle to the finding of any sort of table. Even supposing you can find the publication itself, finding the needed table from the index is the next problem. If you are the originator, or the packager, of a batch of evaluated technical data and you package it in such a manner as to build in problems of upkeep of the set, you are cutting your own throat, or the throats of those who will try to find the material. You are also cutting the throats of those who do not know of the actual existence of whatever evaluated technical data you have foisted on the public, but who suspect that it may exist and want to find it.

LABELING THE UNITS

A compilation, or a data center, can be called a pool in the informational mainstream. This is the place for you to fish for the particular solution, the particular answers that you need. Suppose you infer from the title of Touloukian's thing, or from Timmerman's *Physical Chemical Constants of Binary Systems and Concentrated Solutions,* that it may contain a tabulation which gives you the information you are looking for. Perhaps it is worth thirty thousand or two million dollars to you, so that you do not have to repeat certain experiments. You check the thing or you have someone check it for you. You specify as elaborately, or as precisely, as possible just what it is you need. Can the data that you need be inferred from some table? Can the table be properly interpreted? What language is it in? If it is in a foreign language or if it is published in Britain, do you have problems connected with the terminology? Is their comma a decimal point? If they say "billion," do they mean American billion or British billion? A British billion is a million million. Niobium and columbium are used to mean the same substance, the same element. The metallurgists usually say "columbium." The chemists say "niobium." Furthermore, the chemists have decided on a marvelous international standardization: all the chemists all over the world will say niobium hereafter and all the metallurgists will still say columbium. It is the same stuff. It is too much to expect every indexer to remember to put in cross references when he is preparing an outline. Not every indexer knows that niobium is columbium.

The degree of sophistication that has to be applied in the interpretation of tables produced within your own country is about two or three orders below the degree of sophistication that has to apply when you use tables which were produced in another country. You may say, well, why not do the research over? That depends on whether or not an intelligent and systematic interpretation and translation of these terms can be made to re-express the substantive calculations or data which you need. If it costs thirty thousand dollars in time and energy to recalculate and re-establish the data, in form compatible with what you are trying to do, then this may be perfectly worthwhile if it would take you two million dollars to reproduce the material otherwise. That is a problem for management.

When you label material, when you are labeling material that you are going to inflict on the public, and you use abbreviations which are peculiar to your own way of thinking, do not fail to give, for the use of the public, some indication of, (1) what these abbreviations are intended to stand for; (2) what standard you are using. For instance the meter, or if you have "fl" meaning fluid and someone infers that it means "femtoliter," the effect can be a little hilarious. It is even more interesting when you come across "2m" and the *Encyclopaedia Britannica* uses "m" to mean "mile" and almost everyone else uses it to mean "meter."

Problems arise about whether the term "ton" or "barrel" is used in the sense of a particular trade; or whether "mile" means a geodetic mile or a statute mile. The geodetic system in the United States adopted a mile and put milestones. They can't move the milestones. At least they think they can't move the milestones, and these miles are sufficiently different to throw people off in their calculations from statute miles.

Review

To review the procedures. You find a compilation through a finding guide. For instance, in one of the first five or six items on the list you find a table (through the index of the compilation) and then you try to interpret the table. To say that any given specialist ought to be capable of interpreting (or even guessing at the existence of) all the various factors in the interpretation of any given table, is asking considerably too much. But, to require, or to ask, that the originator, the packager, of any batch of evaluated technical data, indicate the standards he was using, and the meaning of his abbreviations, is only to require what the government requires of people who label products that are put onto the market. As far as the motivation for doing so is concerned, it is entirely different. If you are preparing to publish a batch of evaluated technical data, the question arises of how much time you are free to spend, how much time your organization would allow you to spend, on making this material recoverable and intelligible to those who have to recover it. This is a management problem. It may be that the boiling point you have to recover is your own. It may be that five years later you will have to interpret your own data and you will not be able to do this without an astonishing memory or a batch of reference points which you established at the time you turned the information loose.

Abbreviations

Research on the microminiaturization of crystal balls and hazel twigs, etc., may be going forward as fast as necessary, but I am not sure that the present scientific temper permits us to expect the customary use of crystal balls in interpreting tables of technical data. Therefore labeling is a key to finding out of what the packager meant when he wrote.

A series of new metric prefixes have been at least tentatively adopted; the *femto* and *atto* strike me as being peculiarly subject to confusion. "Fl." meaning *femtoliter* would be exactly the same as the abbreviation of "fluid." It may be that the context will show you perfectly well that it does not mean fluid. But not necessarily. The use of "attometer" (ten to the minus eighteen meters) would seem to be an "atommeter," even if you spell it with double "t." This applies especially in those languages which do not use double letters. Presumably, the Spanish would write it "atometro" and this would be an indication that it stands for some sort of unit for measuring atoms. The suggested abandonment of the liter in scientific work will also cause confusion.

Tolerances

The question of whether a given batch of information is evaluated and precise enough for you is not necessarily something that should be left to your data processing center; an answer which is perfectly acceptable within certain tolerances, can be found perhaps from one sort of table. Perhaps the *International Critical Tables,* even though forty years old, would give you a perfectly acceptable answer within certain tolerances, depending on what you are trying to do with it. If you simply want to find out whether something is about half of the figure for something else, fine. But, if you need something very precise, then you might have to evaluate all the factors involved. This is something which normally a librarian can look up for you, but he has to have some concept of how precise you have to be, and whether or not the background factors can be found, and whether they are pertinent. It may be that you have to go to the original data, the articles on which the compilations were based, to make some sort of judgment on the degree of accuracy originally obtained and the degree of convertibility of the material.

With regard to Landolt-Börnstein, the tables are apparently the latest thing for all sorts of purposes. A new set has been out since 1961. To what extent it has been fully revised and fully updated; to what extent it has been properly labeled to indicate what bases were being used, of terminology and of standardization, is something which ought to be indicated with regard to each table. It may be that the editors felt that the only thing that could be done was to leave this to the researcher. If you need to reassure yourself, you may have to go to the original papers. The classic example of bad tables manners was the bureau chief who decided to reprint a "very useful" table. It was something that had come out in Germany. He didn't bother giving the source at all. Eventually someone asked if the table could be reprinted, because it was so useful. It was found that the table had repeated all the mistakes in a certain German publication, and added a few more. One publication has a list of errata of the tables that it mentions or describes. In other words, someone went through and tried to make sure that all of the errors in the original tables were corrected in this publication, which did not reprint the tables, but told where they were. The next step was to issue an "errata to the errata." A certain degree of perseverance is required in pinning all these things down.

Suppose you ask a librarian to give you only the evaluated and fully reliable material. It seems to me that you are making the kind of request that a Shakespeare scholar might make if he tells the librarian that he wants only the "reliable" material on the Shakespeare-Bacon controversy or on the chronology of Shakespeare's writing. It implies a certain abdication of judgment. This may be entirely reasonable if you have a librarian who is in a position to dig back through these things and verify the timing and the standards used and check up on commentaries, book reviews, etc., which discuss any given compilation and indicate just how reliable it is likely to be.

The originator, or the person who is charged with packaging and launching any given batch of material, has the decision to make of trying to get rid of it, so that it won't be a nuisance to anyone; storing it as it is; storing it and announcing it; refining it and publishing it; packaging it and labeling it and attempting to make it fully acceptable, fully valid and retrievable. In putting this sort of thing out, you can label it so that all the bibliographers will refer to it in the same way. If you have an article to publish which has a large number of tables, if you are in a position to choose which of the various journals it is going into, the rational thing to do is to choose that journal which has a title which can be easily recognized and will not be mis-cited. Thus, for example, if there is something called the *Journal of Steel Research* it is very hard to guess whether a given clerk will file that under *Journal, Steel,* or *Journal of* . . . There are various approaches to filing and therefore, the choice of a title for a journal (or the name of an organization) which eliminates the probability of filing confusion, is a part of the labeling of your data.

If you are able to cite *"Steel Res. J."* meaning *"Steel Research Journal,"* which is hard to misinterpret; this is a good label. But, if you have to cite *"Journal of the Steel Research Society,"* you are immediately building several problems into the citation. Is it going to be found under *"Steel, Research Society Journal"* as librarians always file it (and about half the bibliographers) or is it going to be under "Journal, Steel Research Society," or "Journal *of the* Steel Research Society." The point is that if the journal of publication of your data has a bibliographic handle of wet spaghetti, the effect is that your material may not be found. A negative response will be more likely whenever someone makes a check, and perhaps does not have the time or imagination to check all possibilities.

DISCUSSION

FROM THE FLOOR: In the government, there are many numbers that are attached to documents and reports. What do you think of a universal numbering system?

BIRCH: I think it would be wonderful. At present, a first step exists in the form of a guide to report number series. This publication is available from the Special Libraries Association. It was produced about two years ago and, when you have a report number, when you are planning to start using a series of report numbers, a quick check in this will serve the same sort of function as a trademark check. For instance, I was informed recently, to my dismay, that someone was planning to issue a series numbered "TID-1." To reference librarians "TID" means a series from the AEC (Atomic Energy Commission) which has now gone into the many thousands. To have another series of "TID" inflicted on the public would produce what I think the computer people like to refer to as "noise." Just how much noise, how much trouble, is something else again. The idea of a universal numbering system for publications has been broached. I think that there are certain more immediate steps which could be taken to clear up messes which ought to have priority. I prepared a list of the main rocks and shoals to be avoided in making the titles of journals and the names of organizations file-worthy. This appeared in the *Short Papers of the American Documentation Institute* meeting in Chicago, October 1963.

One of the things that I wanted to stress was the need for packaging the data in a manageable way, then labeling the package, and labeling each element of its contents, in such a way that the interpretation does not require further vast research and crystal-ball gazing.

FROM THE FLOOR: Have you any ideas as to how, in this era of digital storage, the originator, not the processor, can help in this process of preparing his data so that it can be treated by means other than manual?

BIRCH: The processes whereby he can identify it for the computer depend to certain extent on the degree to which he can make it specific. The labeling has to depend on either terminology or on a report-number-type approach. If a batch of material cannot be further sub-identified, it can simply be described in some announcement as "the material which was produced in connection with such-and-such an operation". The possible user may get a hint as to just what sort of use he can make of it. The labeling of such material presupposes some sort of reference to its origin, possibly to the contract under which it was produced. The material itself can be fed into a data center as bits of information, which in turn can be pulled out as bits and then perhaps referred for context to their source. The bibliographic description or the "computerographic" description of any given batch of information has to depend on factors which are peculiar. The stress here is on the need for labeling. To make data findable, label it for someone who does not know of its existence or who uses a subject approach.

At present and for the next ten or fifteen years, most of this sort of thing will have to be done by getting groups of people highly conscious of whatever has been developed in any given field and getting them to keep up with the sources of material and their relationship to each other. The data-center people have to use their memories and their judgment and their imagination to interpret and to mediate between the researcher and the information. The labeling of computer-generated data has to follow approximately the same basic principles as the other, except that there is so much, such large quantities of it, that, unless it is fed into new computer tape and so forth, it is not likely to be sought as separate bits.

The Library of Congress does not attempt to list each item in a batch. Usually they will indicate that "these papers are related to such and such a period" and a researcher who needs them can then go to particular indexes for that batch.

FROM THE FLOOR: Do you want to touch on the obsolescence factors of indexing-concepts, the fact that things do change.

BIRCH: I mentioned "fossil terminology." Suppose someone referred to "consumption," or attempted to use the expression "TB" or "tuberculosis" as an indexing term to find material in medical journals seventy years old. The various terms which have been used, from period to period, would have to be considered in approximately the same way as the various standardizations of the inch and the meter. Thus, seventy years ago "consumption" was the commonplace term for what we now call tuberculosis or TB. If you look in an index under tuberculosis you may find what you are looking for. If you look in an old index under TB or tuberculosis you are quite likely to find nothing, not even a cross-reference to "consumption." Similarly, polio; it is now fairly commonly called polio. You might find it under poliomyelitis in most publications. Anything over twenty or thirty years old will probably have it under "infantile paralysis". The same sort of adjustment of terminology and of approach has to be made in seeking older information of any sort.

There is another problem here, with regard to indexing. The indexer is usually a pigeon-hole-ist. He puts things into pigeon-holes which already exist. If he is paid to think, he may originate pigeon-holes. This may make for confusion; an indexer may be told not to originate pigeon-holes, but to leave that up to the "new-pigeon-hole division". The effect of this is that the indexer puts into pigeon-holes that already exist any new element of information, even if he recognizes it as new. Furthermore, there is an inertia whereby the indexer will almost automatically, if he has a quota to meet, and depending on how much he has been paid or how much time he is allowed, exclude that which is peculiar or novel in a document. The indexer will index those things–those terms, those concepts–which are familiar. This is a phenomenon which I have never found properly discussed. People discuss the need for closer indexing, and things such as that. If you are writing an article, you can use a little indexmanship, either by the way you write, starting each paragraph with the key concept, or by being emphatic enough about what you consider to be novel. The indexer may be led to acknowledge at least *your* novelties, even though he misses everyone else's. Indexmanship is parallel to gamesmanship. It ought to become as commonplace as writing. Indexmanship might even be used as a technique of getting the *writer* to think over what he is presenting and to plan what he is trying to write.

It seems to me, that the appropriate pattern, in making any compilation or book, is to draft an index first, indicating what topics are to be treated, and indicating where in the publication these index elements will be given their primary treatment. Then when you write, you have an outline all ready for you. You can give the primary treatment where it belongs and you won't have to worry about whether the indexer will be able to handle your material properly. Your list of topics can be recast into a formal index by an indexer or by the author. The lack of this sort of approach is illustrated in much of the bad indexing which is done. A major publisher put out an encyclopedia. I have been informed that *after* the pages were in proof, the editors were turned loose to make the index, and ended up with such things as "columbium" and "niobium" as separate entries in the index. There was a certain amount of cross-reference. But why should there be one batch of things under columbium and another batch under niobium? The trouble is, apparently, that they had already gotten the thing into page proof; they couldn't eliminate this obvious nonsense and, therefore, they tried to live with it.

If they had planned the index first, they could have eliminated a great deal of the duplication of effort that goes into most encyclopedias. One author goes hog-wild and includes everything that he is expert on; another fails to include materials which are highly pertinent to his subject. This sort of thing could be caught early if the indexing were planned as the first stage of the planning of any encyclopedia, or of any publication at all.

NUMERICAL DATA RETRIEVAL REPRESENTATIVE PUBLICATIONS

Guides, etc.

1. *Current research and development in scientific documentation.* No. 11, November 1962. (NSF Publication number NSF-63-5.) Washington, National Science Foundation. 440 pp.

   Directory of projects under way, with indexes by subject, sponsor, researcher, and including glossary and interpretation of acronyms. New editions appear each year or half-year. A bibliography is being prepared of the articles pertinent to each project.

2. *Directory of continuing numerical data projects: a survey and analysis by the Office of Critical Tables.* Washington, National Academy of Sciences—National Research Council (Publication 837) 1961. 66 pp.

   Includes indexes of compound-types, projects, researchers, and organizations.

3. *Guide to special issues and indexes of periodicals.* Edited by Doris B. Katz, and others. New York, Special Libraries Association, 1962. 125 pp.

4. *Nonconventional technical information systems in current use.* No. 3, October 1962 (NSF Publication NSF-62-34) Washington, U. S. National Science Foundation. 209 pp.

   Lists organizations and describes activities; indexed by subject, sponsor, researcher, and place.

5. T. E. R. Singer, *Information and communication practice in industry.* (New York, Reinhold, 1958.) Chapter by Ethaline Cortelyou entitled, "Some Fundamentals of Designing Tables of Data," pp. 250–265.

6. *Specialized science information service in the United States: a directory . . . physical and biological sciences.* Washington, National Science Foundation, 1961. (NSF 61-68; 528 pp.)

   Prepared by the Battelle Memorial Institute, Department of Economics and Information Research.

7. J. Arthur Greenwood, *Guide to tables in mathematical statistics.* (Princeton; Princeton University Press, 1962.) 1014 pp.

   Describes tabulated materials appearing elsewhere.

8. Derrick Henry Lehmer, *Guide to tables in the theory of numbers.* Report 1 of the Subcommittee on Section F, Theory of Numbers, of the Division of Physical Sciences of the National Research Council. (Washington: National Academy of Sciences, National Research Council, 1941.) 177 pp.

Includes errata lists for tables described; also includes errata for errata list.

Tables, etc.

9. Alfred W. Francis, *Critical Solution Temperatures.* Washington, American Chemical Society, 1961; 246 pp.

   Advances in Chemistry Series, No. 31. Includes bibliography, pp. 218-246.

10. Hans-Heinrich Landolt, *Zahlenwerte und Funktionen aus Physik, Chemie, Astronomie, Geophysik, und Technik.* (Berlin; Springer, 1950-) (new edition 1961-).

    About one shelf-yard of tables. Commonly called "Landolt-Börnstein."

11. *Selected values of properties of chemical compounds.* College Station, Texas, Chemical Thermodynamic Properties Center, Agricultural and Mechanical College of Texas.

    Three loose-leaf volumes kept up-to-date by inserts. Prepared under the auspices of the Manufacturing Chemists' Association Research Project, and in conjunction with the American Petroleum Institute Research Project 44. The pattern of this publication effort includes parallel materials on spectral data for infrared, ultraviolet, Raman, mass, and nuclear magnetic resonance phenomena.

12. Jean Timmermans. *The physico-chemical constants of binary systems in concentrated solutions. Vol. 1: Two organic compounds (without hydroxyl derivatives).* (New York, Interscience, 1959- .)

13. Y. S. Touloukian, *Retrieval guide to thermophysical properties research literature.* Prepared at the Thermophysical Properties Research Center, Purdue University, Lafayette, Indiana. (New York: McGraw-Hill, 1960- .)

    1963 volumes called "Volume II" in 3 parts.

14. *Journal of Chemical and Engineering Data.* Washington, American Chemical Society.

    Vol. 9, No. 1 corresponds to January 1964.

    Includes such articles as "The Molar Refraction of Liquid Organosilicon Compounds," with six pages of tables.

NEEDS OF INDUSTRY FOR CRITICAL AND OTHER DATA DERIVED FROM GOVERNMENT CONTRACTS

JOHN I. THOMPSON
President, John I. Thompson Company, Washington, D.C.

The government becomes the possessor of an enormous amount of technical and other data information that are derived from a number of sources and for many diverse reasons. Naturally, this information and data belong in the public domain. Much of it is acquired solely for the purpose of transmitting it to the public under laws based on the government's purpose to promote the general welfare.

For instance, the Department of Agriculture's first purpose on its creation was to acquire and diffuse useful information on agricultural subjects in the most general and comprehensive sense. Other departments have been given similar missions by law; the Census Bureau is probably the oldest. It was specifically spelled out in the Constitution. The need for this data and information is determined by various means. In some instances, industry advisory groups have also been established by law, but in many cases a project for such purposes starts through informal contact between the potential user or more likely a using group and a government agency. Congress, because of its appropriation authority, plays a dominant role in any of the final determinations. It should also be noted that in broadening the fields of standards available to industry, the government agencies conduct special surveys. For many years the acquisition of this information and data was solely for direct management of the government through its laboratories and experiment stations, whereas in recent years statutory authority has been given most agencies for direct acquisition by contract.

In 1946, with the passage of the Research and Marketing Act, the Department of Agriculture for the first time received contractual authority. So if we are talking about deriving from contract, there have been and are presently contracts for obtaining direct basic information.

Other information derives as a by-product in the performance of other government functions. This may be in the form of basic data necessary for utilization in application to specific performance or it may be a spin-off from that performance with otherwise unobvious, unrelated implications. It is under such circumstances that "acquisition" has, for the most part, become separated from "diffusion". Unlike the Department of Agriculture where acquisition is only for diffusion to the public, much of the data and information deriving from government's other contracts (especially for defense and space) is acquired only for the purpose of performing an expressed mission, such as a "weapons system," or a "space vehicle." It is true that the applicable NASA statute expressly provides for "the widest practicable and appropriate dissemination"; however, its specific appropriations are, for a great part, tied to the performance of specific missions. I doubt that statutory authority exists for acquiring government rights to all data and information, at least that which is beyond the purposes of the contract itself. Such efforts persist, however, but I would suggest that at a much greater cost and certainly with less effectiveness than if diffusion or dissemination were bartered for. Of course, the "how" of this is not my subject. It may well be that a number of methods need to be employed. A basic policy enunciating the requirement for dissemination of data (acquired during performance under specified contracts) as a coequal product with the other deliverable items would be a fine starting point. Actually, in NASA's case something like this is possible now.

It is important to note that, in general, industry is not unaware of the existence of "data" held in the public domain. Government acquisition of industrial information has, of course, a much shorter history than in the agricultural area.

When Herbert Hoover was Secretary of Commerce, many new functions involving data acquisition first appeared. The Bureau of Standards, for instance, published data on "properties of materials." They soon went way beyond that in Hoover's time. Its awareness shows up even in books such as Lee Bristol's *Profits and Advance,* written in 1931, where his chapter entitled "We Have It in Washington" (about 20 percent of the whole book) is devoted entirely to the data and information available in the government. Industrial needs vary greatly from industry to industry.

A fuller exposure of the entire problem may be helpful. In the first place, we must assume by Industry, we mean American private Industry. The problem is very much different in a monolithic society such as the U.S.S.R. In American industry, the individuals and the corporations exist to make profits. To do this, they must supply all demands, however created, of their customers. The common limitation is "price" versus "utility." It is of cardinal importance to any business, therefore, to continually reduce the cost of producing its products. To accomplish this, there must be a continuing effort to improve and improvement means acquisition of the knowledge of how to improve and subsequent application of that knowledge. This acquisition of knowledge, in itself, whether gained in-house or from other sources, must not be more costly than it is worth. Hence, information and data readily accessible from other sources can be an important factor, very much depending on that source. Also, there is much substance to the theory that, if a project costs less than "X" dollars, it is cheaper to do the project than search the archives to see if it is already done. The value or worth of information must not exceed the cost of obtaining it. Here, obviously accessible Information Centers can play an important part. For the most effective use, these should be classified, for what is important in one area, may be of no interest in another. And, I cite for instance, establishments like the Battelle Defense Metals Information Center, the Armour Institute, and others as examples of classified activities. The extent of public interest governs the numbers and identity of the classifications. In all cases, however, data and information deriving from government contracts should flow in a timely way to the pertinent center together with its other acquisitions. This can best be done if provided for by some systemization and authority.

Industry, regardless of its product, has a right to availability of data and information derived from work accomplished on government contracts. It is useful in improving the value of its products and services. Systems for information dissemination must recognize information and data collection by industry on a basis that can be selective. Industry must not look for panaceas. They must have a practical viewpoint. They are like the noted molecular biologist who said, "If all of human knowledge could be put on a computer and I could press a button to get all the information on DNA, I doubt that I would ever press a button".

Industry needs the data and information, but will only seek and use it if the instrumentalities involved are not cumbersome and if they provide an opportunity for selectivity. Again we are talking about a free competitive enterprise system in which judgment must play a great part in getting there "firstest with the mostest". I now revert to the need for selectivity. Industrial requirements for information will always be selective, whether bidding on and performing work for the government or not. Information and data accumulated on other government contracts has an important bearing on industrial competition. There are a number of dissemination systems available, however, such as that furnished by the Defense Documentation Center, etc. These are continually improving their mechanisms. The problem is always one of timeliness and completeness of inputs. Obtaining the delivery of discovered data and information under government contracts as a coequal requirement with the delivery of the products or services are the primary concern of the government "Data" Banks.

I have said that our system is a "private enterprise" one. Its incentive is profit. True, to some individuals, other incentives may apply but for the total system, "profit" is the incentive. We have government sources for dissemination, supply of enormous proportions. Firms largely engaged in government contracting utilize these because it is profitable to do so. We have, also, many thoughtful persons almost frantically decrying the failure of industry (not in government business) to avail themselves of this data and information. You hear of all the efforts to effect "fallout" and yet we see so little actually entering the economy as a result of work accomplished under government contracts. I feel it pertinent to comment on this aspect.

It may help to direct attention to information and data that industry actually will use and explain why there is a lack of interest and hence need in other areas. As our system is built upon the individual, we can not expect to force applications of these improvements merely through the knowledge that they appear to be improvements. Assuming that the system for ferreting out and disseminating works up to the point where a new user could acquire rights from the "public domain," there is no assurance that such potential user would apply the improvement unless he has considerable incentive to do so. It is to these incentives that I wish to direct my remarks. The present statutes relative to "Patent Rights" under which the government operates in many aspects motivate against providing the obvious incentive, "an exclusive license". It is quite possible, however, that in certain instances for a different purpose, possibilities exist for obtaining licenses adequate for protection of the "market". Thus, although the invention be derived from one discovered and applied in the actual government project, the new usage leads to adequate separate coverage.

I think we must recognize that whenever government-acquired information or data is such that it becomes patentable, there is little interest to other firms except in a negative way. Furthermore, no individual or firm will expend large sums developing a market for something that is also available to his competitors.

The information and data needed by industry comprises the basic additions to our body of knowledge, the material and environmental characteristics, statistical innovations, new physical laws, newly discovered and explained phenomena. These are ideas that must be channeled into the Information Centers or otherwise be made available to industry. They constitute a primary need and their availability would result in use without discrimination.

In summary, there are three points concerning needs of industry. First, there should be a recognition of potential information deriving from a government contract and that at its inception steps should be taken for its timely and effective dissemination. Secondly, industry will always remain selective in its acquisition of government data and information and this fact should be recognized in the systems devised for such dissemination. Thirdly, there will always be far less utilization of data and information discovered first and of a patentable or copyright nature under government contract than its discoverers or their administrative people will expect.

It will be a long time before serendipity will be replaced. Our creative thought process is often stimulated by apparently nonpertinent ideas. How to take this human trait into account when dealing with information, storage, and retrieval systems is, of course, the problem.

DISCUSSION

FROM THE FLOOR: Certain firms insist on keeping information which they have derived "confidential." They are willing to turn it over to the government only with the idea that it will not be released to the competitive company that didn't spend any money to derive these facts.

JOHN I. THOMPSON: We have a lot of variations possible. It depends largely on the input. Take some large aircraft organization that looms large on the financial scene. If it is doing and has done 93 percent of its business with the government, there is a great deal more opportunity for the government to claim all data under "public domain" than they could from the General Electric Company, which does a much smaller fraction of its business with the Federal agencies. It is largely a matter of trying to trace where the dollars are derived and for what purpose. The government could well contract for all rights if it were understood at the time of writing the contract. Under such a "contract," they should pay for the dissemination of information that is not directly concerned with the objective of the contract. The contractor always has a right to accept or refuse such terms. Where we are not clear on these principles, we run into trouble. There is always the question as to what constitutes information; to whom does it belong; whence was it derived. It should be cleared up as a national policy. For instance, when the Department of Agriculture sets forth its intention to contract, the intent is clear. When it develops a way of freezing concentrated orange juice, it becomes a "public" product. The Congress appropriated the money for it. But when we get into many other areas, such as when NASA calls for the development of a substance to line the molds for solid fuels, we may have something else. For instance, a hat manufacturer in Kansas City or St. Louis may find a use for this material. Should he pay for this usage?

FROM THE FLOOR: Another problem has been how you obtain more products in the civil economy that derive from government contracts. Do you really believe that if the information centers would distribute more information, that this would occur?

JOHN I. THOMPSON: I was referring to the information that is not proprietary; rather it is basic. Environmental data and information should be quickly published. For instance, my company is working under contract to obtain certain environmental data concerning oceanography. It is already several years old and should have been made available long ago.

FROM THE FLOOR: How large an operation do you run in the information center area?

JOHN I. THOMPSON: We are in the information business in a variety of ways. It may be 20 percent of our total business.

FROM THE FLOOR: Are you satisfied that the NASA approach of hiring the University of Indiana to establish an "Aerospace Research Application Center" is the best way to disseminate government technical data?

JOHN I. THOMPSON: No, I am not, but you must realize that this is the best that NASA can probably do under the existing law. Don't forget that there is an established policy that under any NASA contract any development is the property of the United States government unless a waiver is issued.

FROM THE FLOOR: I take it that you don't care for this policy.

JOHN I. THOMPSON: No, I don't. I would add that it is the best job that can be done under the law when the information produced lies in the public domain. It is good to have wide dissemination of knowledge and don't forget "serendipity." I mean a lot of ideas result from other stimulation and as long as thinking people express their concepts on paper, we do derive some benefit, but the "grab-bag" method of allowing everyone to catch at the same time does not maximize on our total potential.

FROM THE FLOOR: What do you feel that industry can do? Every-time we get around to the subject, it is always what can the government do? What can industry do in the way of getting information into the information centers, or into publication? What actions can they take that won't jeopardize their proprietary rights?

JOHN I. THOMPSON: Well, I think that in most instances industry is pretty liberal with its by-product of basic knowledge, environmental knowledge, or materials characteristic knowledge, that it derives in its studies. Much is made known through Industrial Associations. Perhaps some additional education would be helpful directed towards encouraging industrial management to appreciate to a greater extent the desirability of participating in more industrial and professional society technical meetings.

FROM THE FLOOR: I wonder if we appreciate that the standards work in our professional societies is a tremendous common meeting ground for encouraging industrial people to exchange information.

JOHN I. THOMPSON: This is right.

FROM THE FLOOR: As the operator of one or more information centers, can you see a *modus operandi* that could be put into effect to better work with the professional societies right now? In other words, why shouldn't the professional societies be feeding their information into somebody's information center?

JOHN I. THOMPSON: I believe this should be so. Of course, there is the cost of doing this. You aren't going to accomplish it by edict, but by promotion, such as EJC's more recent efforts. This could be done and of course, again, it all calls for some funds. It may be that public funds could be employed.